Biology

Cells
Unit 2
Resource Book

Printed in the United States of America.

ISBN-13: 978-0-618-72523-6   ISBN-10: 0-618-72523-7

6 7 8 9 - 1421 - 12 11 10
4500247222

Cells
Unit 2 Resource Book

CHAPTER 3 CELL STRUCTURE AND FUNCTION

CHAPTER 4 CELLS AND ENERGY

CHAPTER 5 CELL GROWTH AND DIVISION

UNIT 2 CELLS

Name Period Date

SECTION 3.1 | CELL THEORY

Study Guide

KEY CONCEPT

Cells are the basic unit of life.

VOCABULARY		
cell theory	organelle	eukaryotic cell
cytoplasm	prokaryotic cell	

MAIN IDEA: Early studies led to the development of the cell theory.

In a phrase, tell what each scientist did to help develop the cell theory.

Scientist	Contribution to Cell Theory
1. Hooke	
2. Leeuwenhoek	
3. Schleiden	
4. Schwann	
5. Virchow	

6. What are the three parts of the cell theory?

____

____

____

7. Give two reasons why the cell theory is important.

____

____

Name Period Date

MAIN IDEA: Prokaryotic cells lack a nucleus and most internal structures of eukaryotic cells.

In the top left side of the Y shape below, write the characteristics of eukaryotic cells. In the top right side of the Y shape below, write the characteristics of prokaryotic cells. At the bottom of the Y shape below, write the characteristics that both kinds of cells have in common. Then lightly cross out those characteristics at the top of the Y.

Eukaryotic cells	Prokaryotic cells
______________	______________
______________	______________
______________	______________
______________	______________

Both

____

____

____

____

Vocabulary Check

8. What is cytoplasm?

____

9. Where do you find organelles?

____

10. What statements summarize scientists' concepts of cells?

____

11. Which type of cells have no nucleus?

____

Name Period Date

SECTION 3.1 | CELL THEORY

Power Notes

Scientists who contributed to the cell theory:	The principles of cell theory:
Important technological advances:	**1.** **2.** **3.** The cell theory is:

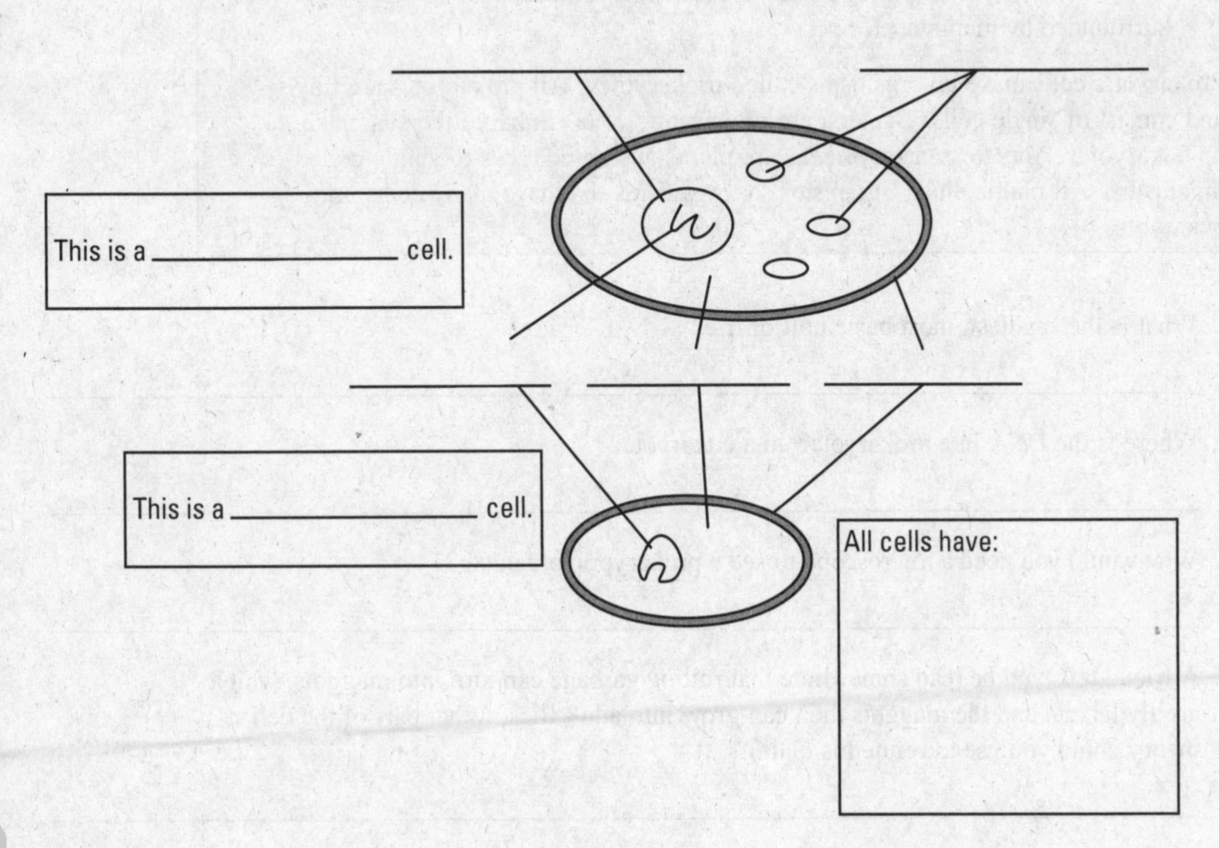

Name Period Date

SECTION 3.1 | CELL THEORY

Reinforcement

KEY CONCEPT Cells are the basic unit of life.

The invention of the microscope in the late 1500s revealed to early scientists a whole new world of tiny cells. Most cells are so small that they cannot be seen without a microscope. The discoveries of scientists from the 1600s through the 1800s led to the cell theory, which is a unifying concept of biology. The **cell theory** has three major principles:

- All organisms are made of cells.
- All existing cells are produced by other living cells.
- The cell is the most basic unit of life.

All cells can be divided into two major groups: **prokaryotic cells** or **eukaryotic cells.** The main differences between the two kinds of cells are in their structure:

- Eukaryotic cells have a nucleus defined by a membrane, while prokaryotic cells have no nucleus.
- In eukaryotic cells, the DNA, or genetic information, is found in the nucleus. In prokaryotic cells, the DNA is found in the **cytoplasm,** the jellylike substance that fills both types of cells.
- Eukaryotic cells have **organelles,** structures that perform jobs for a cell. Most organelles are surrounded by membranes. Prokaryotic cells do not have organelles surrounded by membranes.

Prokaryotic cells make up organisms called prokaryotes. All prokaryotes are tiny and consist of single cells. Bacteria are prokaryotic cells. Eukaryotic cells make up eukaryotes. You are a eukaryote, as are plants and some types of single-celled organisms. All multicellular organisms, or organisms that have many cells, are eukaryotes.

1. What is the smallest, most basic unit of life?

____

2. Where is the DNA in a prokaryote? in a eukaryote?

____

3. Why would you need a microscope to see a prokaryotic organism?

____

4. A friend tells you he read somewhere that rotting garbage can turn into maggots, which are fly larvae, and the maggots then can grow into adult flies. What part of the cell theory could you use to refute his claim?

____

Name Period Date

SECTION 3.2 | CELL ORGANELLES

Study Guide

KEY CONCEPT

Eukaryotic cells share many similarities.

VOCABULARY		
cytoskeleton	Golgi apparatus	lysosome
nucleus	vesicle	centriole
endoplasmic reticulum	mitochondrion	cell wall
ribosome	vacuole	chloroplast

MAIN IDEA: Cells have an internal structure.

1. Look at Figure 3.5 in your textbook. What are the functions of a cytoskeleton?

____

____

2. How is a cytoskeleton like your skeleton?

____

3. How is a cytoskeleton like your muscles?

____

MAIN IDEA: Several organelles are involved in making and processing proteins.
Write either the function or the name of each organelle. Draw a sketch to help you remember it.

Organelle	Function	Sketch
4. nucleus		
5.	helps in the production of proteins and lipids	
6. ribosomes		
7. Golgi apparatus		
8.	carries certain molecules from place to place within a cell	

Name Period Date

MAIN IDEA: Other organelles have various functions.

Write the function of each organelle. Draw a sketch to help you remember it.

Organelle	Function	Sketch
9. mitochondrion		
10. vacuole		
11. lysosome		
12. centriole		

MAIN IDEA: Plant cells have cell walls and chloroplasts.

13. What role do cell walls play in a plant?

14. What is the difference between a cell wall and a cell membrane?

15. Why are chloroplasts important?

Vocabulary Check

16. Which cell part is a maze of folded membranes where proteins and lipids are produced?

17. Which cell part converts food into energy that is usable by a cell?

SECTION 3.2 | CELL ORGANELLES

Power Notes

Cell Organelle	Organelle Function	Organelle Image

Name Period Date

SECTION 3.2 | CELL ORGANELLES
Reinforcement

KEY CONCEPT Eukaryotic cells share many similarities.

Plants, animals, and some single-celled organisms are eukaryotes. Eukaryotic cells have an organized internal structure and organelles that are surrounded by membranes. Organelles look different from each other and have different functions. Several have a specific job in making and processing proteins so that a cell can live, function, and reproduce. Plant and animal cells have a lot of the same parts, but a few of their parts are different. The list below tells you what each cell part does.

Part	Job and Description
nucleus	double membrane layer that stores and protects DNA; includes the nucleolus, a dense region where ribosomes are assembled.
endoplasmic reticulum (ER)	network of thin folded membranes that help produce proteins and lipids; two kinds of ER: smooth and rough
ribosomes	tiny round organelles that link amino acids together to form proteins; may be in the cytoplasm or on the ER, which makes it look rough
Golgi apparatus	stacked layers of membranes that sort, package, and deliver proteins
vesicles	little sacs that carry different molecules where they're needed; made and broken down as needed by the cell
mitochondria	bean-shaped organelles that release energy from sugars for the cell
centrioles	found in animal cells; organize microtubules to form cilia and flagella
vacuoles	sacs that store materials for the cell; the materials might be water, food molecules, ions, and enzymes
cell walls	strong layer that protects, supports, and gives shape to plant cells; not found in animal cells
chloroplasts	change energy from the sun into chemical energy for the plant; not found in animal cells
cytoplasm	jellylike substance that fills a cell
cell membrane	double-layer of phospholipids that forms a boundary between a cell and its surrounding environment
lysosomes	membrane-bound organelles that contain enzymes

1. What are two characteristics of eukaryotic cells?

____

____

____

2. What is the function of mitochondria?

____

3. What two organelles are found in plant cells but not in animal cells?

____

Name Period Date

SECTION **3.3** | CELL MEMBRANE

Study Guide

KEY CONCEPT

The cell membrane is a barrier that separates a cell from the external environment.

VOCABULARY	
cell membrane	selective permeability
phospholipid	receptor
fluid mosaic model	

MAIN IDEA: Cell membranes are composed of two phospholipid layers.

1. Draw a phospholipid in the box below. Label the three major parts.

2. Which part of a phospholipid is charged, or polar? __________

3. Which part of a phospholipid is nonpolar? __________

4. What type of molecules interact with water, polar or nonpolar? __________

5. Where does a cell membrane come into contact with water? __________

6. Why do the phospholipids surrounding the cell form a bilayer? __________

A cell membrane has other types of molecules embedded in the phospholipid bilayer. List a function of each type of molecule in the table below.

Molecule	Function
7. Cholesterol	
8. Proteins	
9. Carbohydrates	

Name Period Date

10. In what way is a membrane fluid?

____

11. Draw a picture in the box below to represent selective permeability.

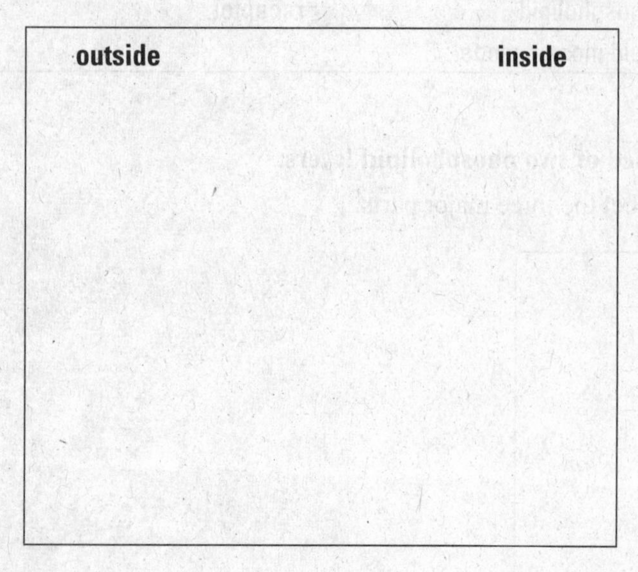

MAIN IDEA: Chemical signals are transmitted across the cell membrane.

12. A ________________ detects a signal molecule and carries out an action in response.

13. A ________________ is a molecule that acts as a signal when it binds to a receptor.

14. A ligand that can cross the cell membrane can bind to an ________________ receptor.

15. A ligand that cannot cross the cell membrane can send a message to a cell by binding to a ________________ receptor, which then ________________ shape.

Vocabulary Check

16. What is the fluid mosaic model?

____

17. The cell membrane allows some, but not all, molecules to cross. What term describes this property?

____

Name Period Date

SECTION 3.3 | CELL MEMBRANE

Power Notes

Cell Membrane

Functions:

Phospholipids:

Fluid mosaic model:

Other molecules:

-
-
-

Sketch a semipermeable membrane.

Selective permeability:

-
-
-
-

Receptors:

- Intracellular
- Membrane

SECTION 3.3 | CELL MEMBRANE

Reinforcement

KEY CONCEPT The cell membrane is a barrier that separates a cell from the external environment.

The **cell membrane** forms a boundary that separates the inside of a cell from the outside environment. It plays an active role by controlling the passage of materials into and out of a cell and by responding to signals. The membrane is made of molecules called **phospholipids,** which consist of three parts: (1) a charged phosphate group; (2) glycerol; (3) two fatty acid chains.

The structure of phospholipids gives them distinct chemical properties. The phosphate group and glycerol form a polar "head." The fatty acid chains form a nonpolar "tail." Cells are both surrounded by water and contain water. In the cell membrane, phospholipids form a double layer, or bilayer. In this way, the polar heads interact with the polar water molecules outside and inside a cell. The nonpolar tails are sandwiched together inside the bilayer, away from the water.

The cell membrane also includes a variety of molecules that give the membrane properties it would not otherwise have.

- Cholesterol molecules make the membrane stronger.
- Proteins help molecules and ions cross the membrane and can act as **receptors,** proteins that detect a signal and respond by performing an action.
- Carbohydrates help cells distinguish one cell type from another.

The **fluid mosaic model** describes the characteristics and makeup of the cell membrane. The phospholipids can slip past each other like a fluid. The membrane is made up of many different molecules, like a mosaic.

The cell membrane has a property called **selective permeability,** which means that it allows some molecules to cross but blocks others. Selective permeability helps a cell maintain homeostasis.

Cells have receptors both in the cell membrane and inside the cell. Receptors help cells communicate with other cells and respond to the environment.

- Membrane receptors bind to signals that cannot cross the cell membrane. They cross the membrane and transmit a message inside the cell by changing shape.
- Intracellular receptors are located inside a cell and bind to molecules that can cross the cell membrane. They may interact with DNA to control certain genes.

1. Why do phospholipids form a bilayer in the cell membrane?

____

2. How does a sieve (or colander) demonstrate the property of selective permeability?

____

Name Period Date

SECTION **3.4** | DIFFUSION AND OSMOSIS
Study Guide

KEY CONCEPT
Materials move across membranes because of concentration differences.

VOCABULARY		
passive transport	osmosis	hypotonic
diffusion	isotonic	facilitated diffusion
concentration gradient	hypertonic	

MAIN IDEA: Diffusion and osmosis are types of passive transport.

1. What is a concentration gradient?

____

2. What does it mean for a molecule to diffuse down a concentration gradient?

____

Complete the concept map below about passive transport.

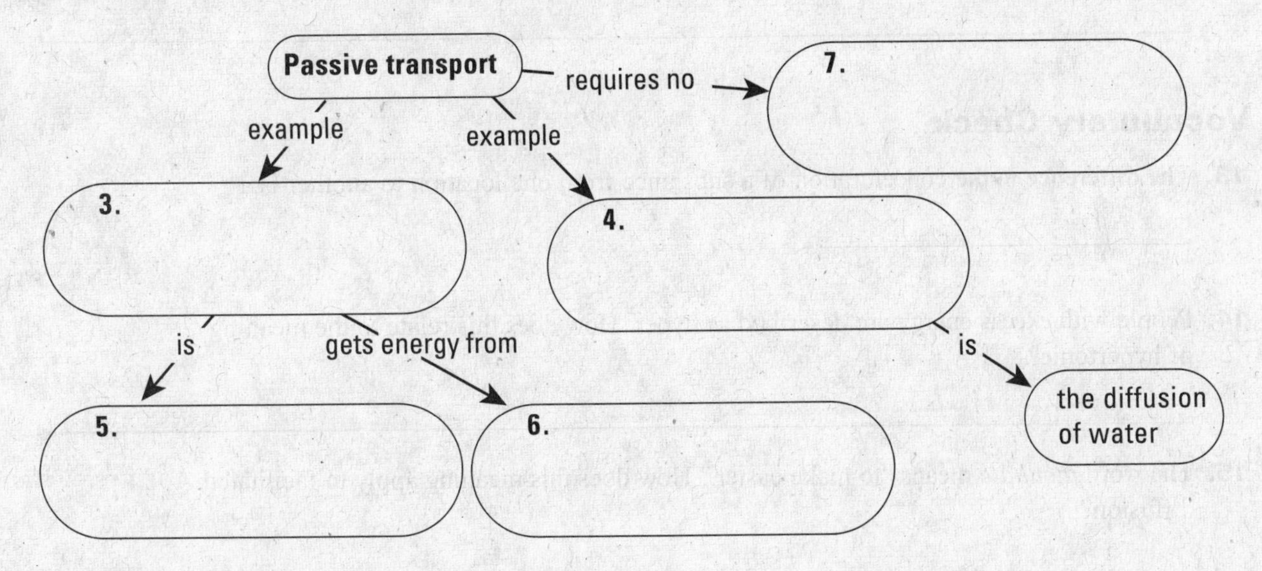

8. The higher the concentration of dissolved particles in a solution, the

_______________ the concentration of water molecules in that solution.

Name Period Date

Suppose you have three solutions with different concentrations of particles. Relative to the concentration of particles in a cell, one solution is isotonic, one is hypertonic, and one is hypotonic. Use this information to answer the next two questions.

9. Which solution has the highest concentration of particles?

____

10. Which solution has the highest concentration of water molecules?

____

MAIN IDEA: Some molecules diffuse through transport proteins.

11. How does facilitated diffusion differ from simple diffusion?

____

____

12. In facilitated diffusion, do molecules move down a concentration gradient or against a concentration gradient?

____

Vocabulary Check

13. The difference in the concentration of a substance from one location to another is a

______________________________.

14. People with excess energy are described as hyper. How does this relate to the meaning of hypertonic?

____

15. The word *facilitate* means "to make easier." How does this meaning apply to facilitated. diffusion?

____

Name Period Date

SECTION **3.4** | DIFFUSION AND OSMOSIS

Power Notes

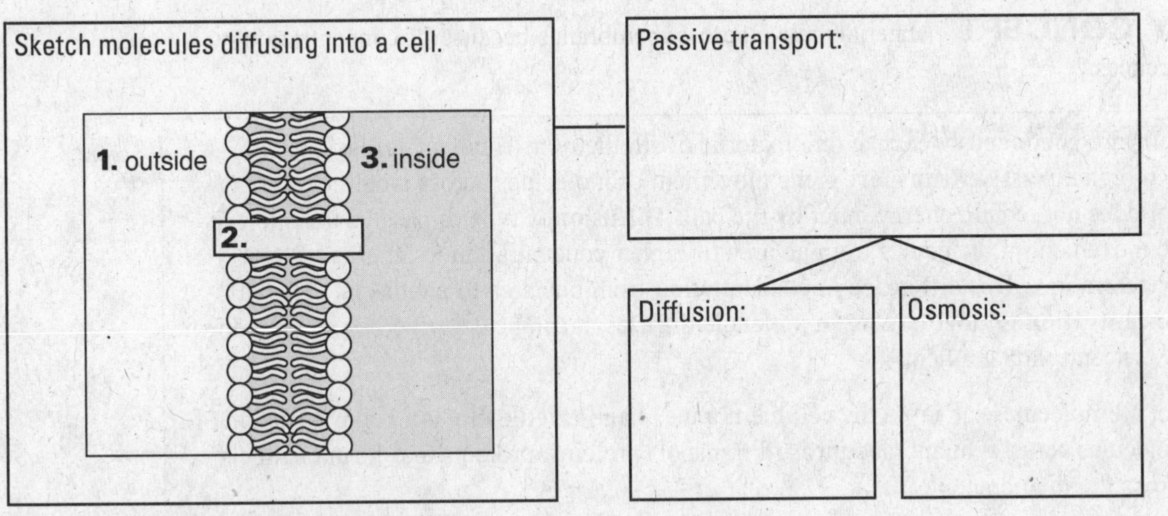

How do different solutions affect cells?

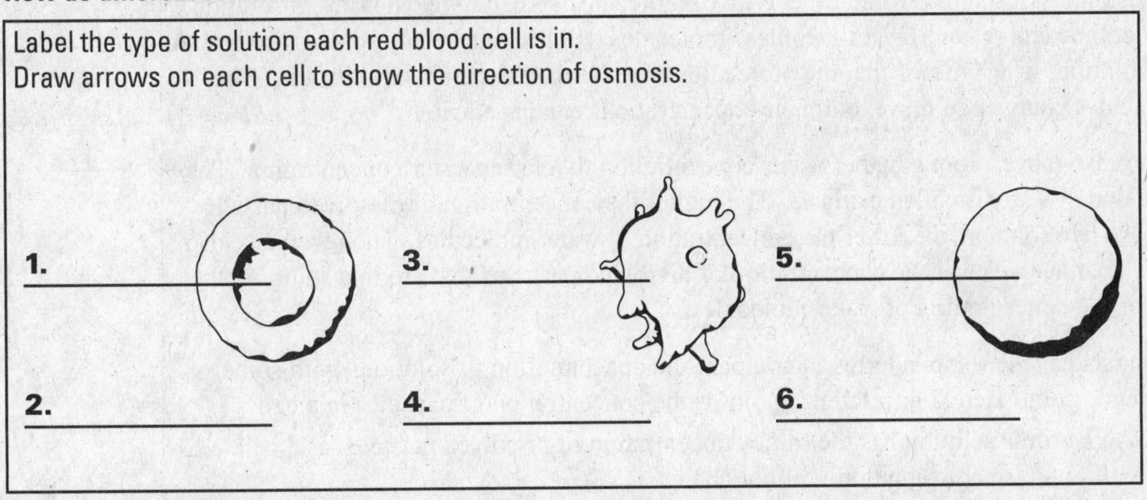

Label the type of solution each red blood cell is in.
Draw arrows on each cell to show the direction of osmosis.
1.
2.
3.
4.
5.
6.

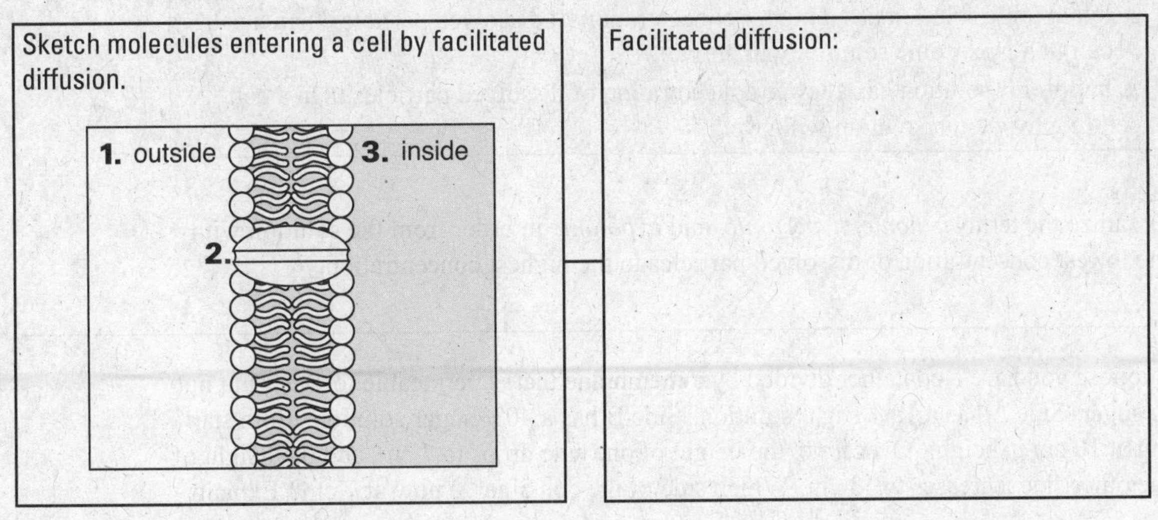

Sketch molecules entering a cell by facilitated diffusion.
1. outside
3. inside
2.
Facilitated diffusion:

Name Period Date

SECTION 3.4 | DIFFUSION AND OSMOSIS

Reinforcement

KEY CONCEPT Materials move across membranes because of concentration differences.

Cells are continuously exchanging materials with their environment across the cell membrane. **Passive transport** is the movement of molecules across a cell membrane that does not require energy input by the cell. **Diffusion,** a type of passive transport, is the movement of molecules from an area of higher concentration to an area of lower concentration. This difference in concentration from one area to another is called a **concentration gradient.** When a molecule diffuses, it can be described as moving down its concentration gradient.

Not all molecules can cross the cell membrane. **Facilitated diffusion** is the diffusion of molecules across a membrane through transport proteins, proteins that form channels across the membrane.

Diffusion is a result of the natural energy of molecules. When molecules are in solution, they collide and scatter. Over time, these molecules will become evenly spread throughout the solution, which means that the molecules have reached dynamic equilibrium. The molecules continue to move, but their concentration remains equal.

Water also moves from a higher water concentration to a lower water concentration. The diffusion of water is called **osmosis.** The higher the concentration of dissolved particles that are in a solution, the lower the concentration of water molecules. The reverse is also true. That is, the lower the concentration of dissolved particles that are in a solution, the higher the concentration of water molecules.

Scientists have developed terms to compare the concentration of solutions with some reference point. Here, our reference point is the concentration of particles in a cell.

- An **isotonic** solution has the same concentration of dissolved particles as a cell. A cell in an isotonic solution will not change.
- A **hypertonic** solution has a higher concentration of dissolved particles than a cell. A cell in a hypertonic solution will shrivel.
- A **hypotonic** solution has a lower concentration of dissolved particles than a cell. A cell in a hypotonic solution will swell.

1. Organize the terms *isotonic, hypertonic,* and *hypotonic* in order from the solution with the lowest concentration of dissolved particles to the highest concentration.

____

2. Suppose you have a container divided by a membrane that is permeable to water but not to sugar. Side A has a 10% sugar solution. Side B has a 40% sugar solution. Both start out at 10 cm in height. Over time, the height of one side drops to 7 cm, and the height of the other side increases to 13 cm. Which side of the container is now at 7 cm? Explain.

____

Name Period Date

SECTION 3.5 | ACTIVE TRANSPORT, ENDOCYTOSIS, AND EXOCYTOSIS

Study Guide

KEY CONCEPT

Cells use energy to transport materials that cannot diffuse across a membrane.

VOCABULARY	
active transport	phagocytosis
endocytosis	exocytosis

MAIN IDEA: Proteins can transport materials against a concentration gradient.

1. How is active transport different than simple diffusion and facilitated diffusion?

____

2. How is active transport similar to facilitated diffusion?

____

3. List two characteristics that almost all transport proteins share.

____

____

4. List the key distinguishing feature of active transport proteins.

____

5. Refer to Figure 3.25 to draw a picture in the box below to represent active transport.

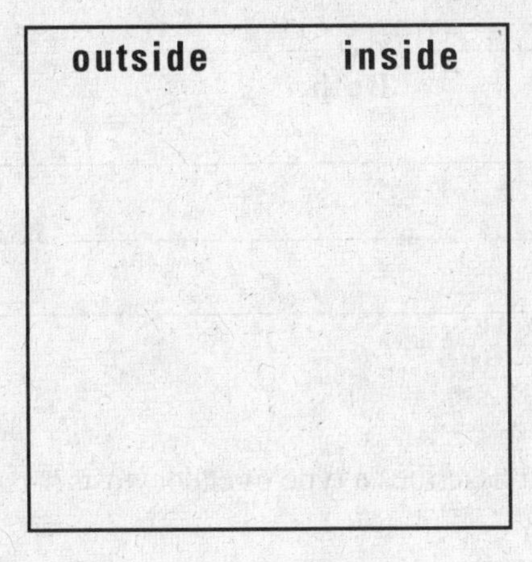

6. Most active transport proteins use energy from the breakdown of _______________.

Name Period Date

MAIN IDEA: Endocytosis and exocytosis transport materials across the membrane in vesicles.

7. A cell may transport a substance in ______________________ if the substance is too large to cross the membrane.

8. During endocytosis, the vesicle membrane fuses with a lysosome, and the membrane and its contents are broken down by ______________________.

Complete the Y diagram below to compare and contrast the processes of endocytosis and exocytosis. Under the heading "endocytosis," list the characteristics of endocytosis. Under the heading "exocytosis," list the characteristics of exocytosis. At the bottom of the Y, write the characteristics that both processes have in common. Then lightly cross out those characteristics at the top of the Y.

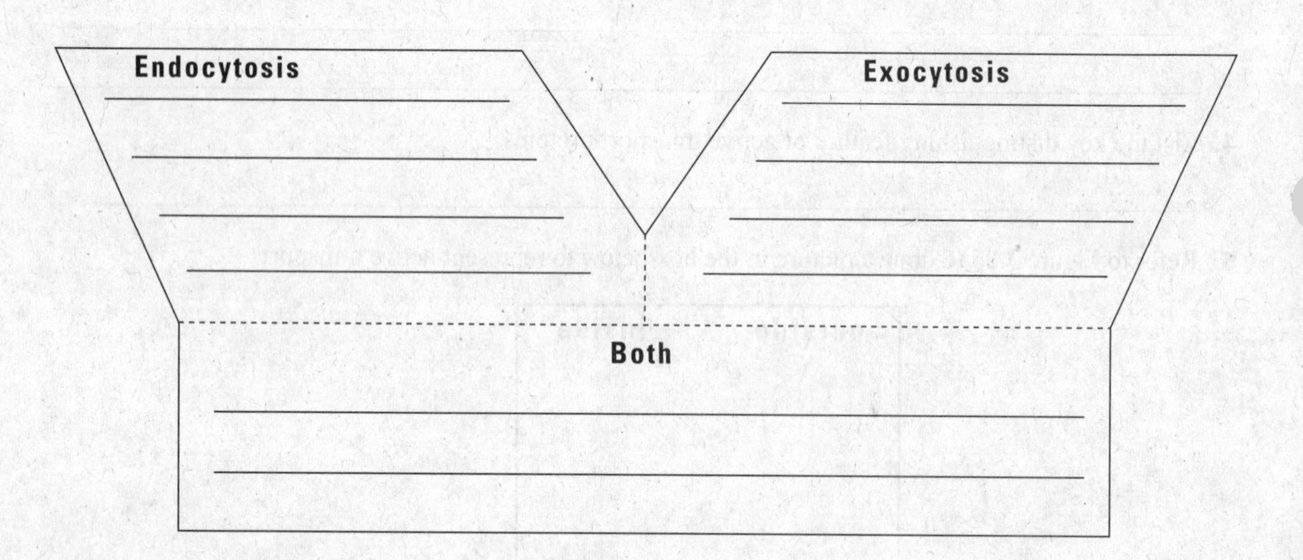

Vocabulary Check

9. What term means "cell eating" and describes a type of endocytosis?

____

10. The prefix *exo-* means "out of," and the prefix *endo-* means "taking in." How do these meanings relate to the meaning of exocytosis and endocytosis?

____

____

11. What process drives molecules across a membrane against a concentration gradient?

____

Name Period Date

SECTION 3.5 | ACTIVE TRANSPORT, ENDOCYTOSIS, AND EXOCYTOSIS

Power Notes

Sketch molecules entering a cell by active transport.

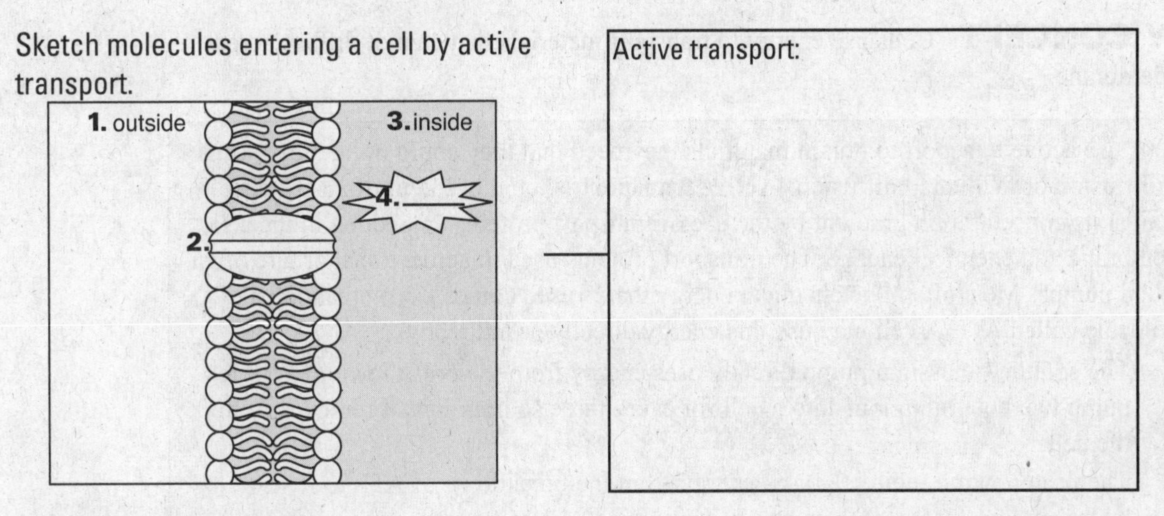

Endocytosis: ______________________________

____

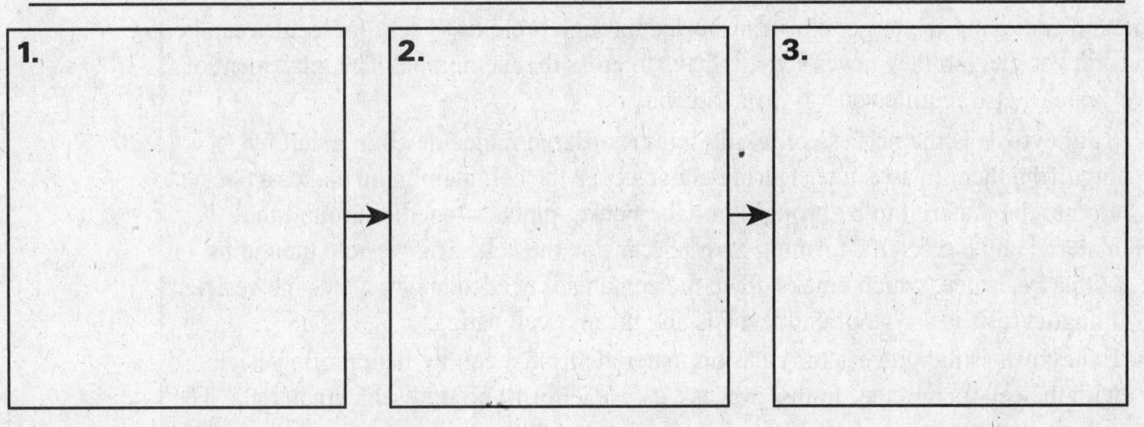

Exocytosis: ______________________________

____

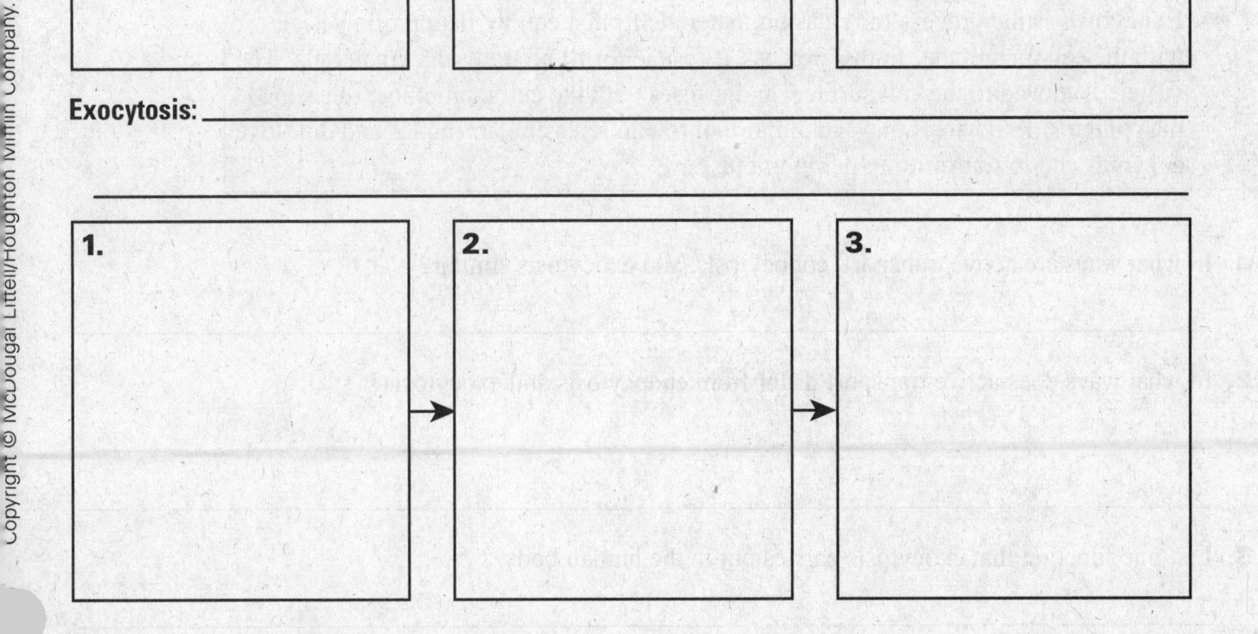

Name Period Date

SECTION **3.5** ACTIVE TRANSPORT, ENDOCYTOSIS, AND EXOCYTOSIS

Reinforcement

KEY CONCEPT Cells use energy to transport materials that cannot diffuse across the membrane.

Cells use active transport to obtain materials they need that they could not get by means of diffusion or facilitated diffusion. **Active transport** is the movement of a substance against its concentration gradient by the use of transport proteins embedded in the cell membrane and chemical energy. The transport proteins used in active transport are often called pumps. Most often, the chemical energy that is used comes from breakdown of a molecule called ATP. A cell may use this energy directly or indirectly.

- The sodium-potassium pump directly uses energy from the breakdown of ATP to pump two potassium ions into a cell for every three sodium ions it removes from the cell.
- The proton pump indirectly uses energy from the breakdown of ATP to remove hydrogen ions (protons) from a cell. This action creates a charge gradient, which is a form of stored energy. This charge gradient can then be used to drive other pumps to transport molecules such as sucrose.

Some molecules are too large to be transported through proteins. These molecules can be moved in vesicles, so they never actually have to cross the membrane. The movement of these vesicles also requires energy from a cell.

- **Endocytosis** is the process of taking liquids or large molecules into a cell by engulfing them in a vesicle. During endocytosis, the cell membrane makes a pocket around the material to be brought in. The pocket pinches together around the material and breaks off, forming a vesicle, inside the cell. This vesicle then joins with a lysosome, which breaks down the contents if needed and recycles the vesicle. **Phagocytosis** is a type of endocytosis and means "cell eating."
- **Exocytosis** is the process of releasing materials from a cell by fusion of a vesicle with the cell membrane. In this process, a vesicle forms around select materials. The vesicle is moved to the cell surface, and it fuses with the cell membrane, releasing the contents. Exocytosis plays an important role in releasing hormones and digestive enzymes and in transmitting nerve impulses.

1. In what ways are active transport, endocytosis, and exocytosis similar?

____

2. In what ways does active transport differ from endocytosis and exocytosis?

____

____

3. List one function that exocytosis carries out in the human body.

____

CHAPTER 3

DEFINING VARIABLES: OPERATIONAL DEFINITIONS

Data Analysis Practice

The operational definition of a variable—a specific description of what is observed and measured in an experiment—is important information when scientists are trying to replicate other scientists' experiments.

A student wants to measure diffusion rates across a semipermeable membrane. The following experiment is carried out:

- A cellulose membrane is placed in each of three aquariums, separating each one in half. Water can cross the membrane, but salt cannot.
- In each aquarium, one side is filled with a 5% solution of NaCl.
- The other side of Aquarium A is filled with a 10% solution of NaCl.
- The other side of Aquarium B is filled with a 20% solution of NaCl.
- The other side of Aquarium C is filled with a 30% solution of NaCl.
- The amount of time for equilibrium to be reached between the two sides in each aquarium was recorded.

Diffusion Rates

Aquarium	Time to Reach Equilibrium (minutes)
A	67
B	32
C	10

1. **Identify** What is the operational definition of the dependent variable in this experiment?

____

____

2. **Analyze** What effect does the concentration of solutes have on diffusion rates?

____

____

3. **Analyze** In Aquarium C, would the water level on the side with 30% solution of NaCl be higher, lower, or equal to the water level on the side with 5% solution? Explain.

____

____

____

CHAPTER 3 | MODELING CELL RECEPTORS

Pre-AP* Activity

You have learned in Chapter 3 that cells have receptors that allow them to respond to signals from the environment and from other cells. Signals may come in many forms, including light, electrical impulses, and molecules. We will focus on signal molecules, or ligands.

RESPONSES

The binding of a receptor to a ligand can trigger many responses. This process is called signal transduction, because the cell is changing (transducing) one type of signal into another. Some of these responses happen right away, such as the cell's rapid rearrangement of its cytoskeleton. Other responses happen slowly, such as the production of new proteins.

The process of converting one signal into another usually involves a chain of events. That is, the binding of a receptor to its ligand makes the receptor active. The receptor then activates another molecule, which then activates another molecule, and so on. In biology, this chain of events is often called a cascade. You can also think of it as a domino effect. Through this domino effect, a small stimulus can have a big effect. For instance, if the binding of a receptor and ligand causes a cell to read a certain gene, that gene might code for a protein that tells the cell to read more genes, making more proteins.

RECEPTORS

The two main types of receptors are membrane receptors and intracellular receptors. Both types of receptors recognize specific ligands, change shape when they bind to a ligand, and trigger a chain of events inside the cell that can have various results. Despite these similarities, membrane receptors and intracellular receptors differ in important ways.

MEMBRANE RECEPTORS

Membrane receptors are proteins located within the cell membrane. One end juts outside the cell membrane, and the other end sticks into the cytoplasm on the inside of the cell. The protein may wind back and forth across the membrane. Ligands that cannot cross the plasma membrane bind to the membrane receptors. These molecules tend to be large or polar, and they do not enter the cell. Instead, the binding of the membrane receptor and the ligand causes the receptor to change shape. This change in shape causes the part of the receptor inside the cell to interact with nearby molecules in new ways.

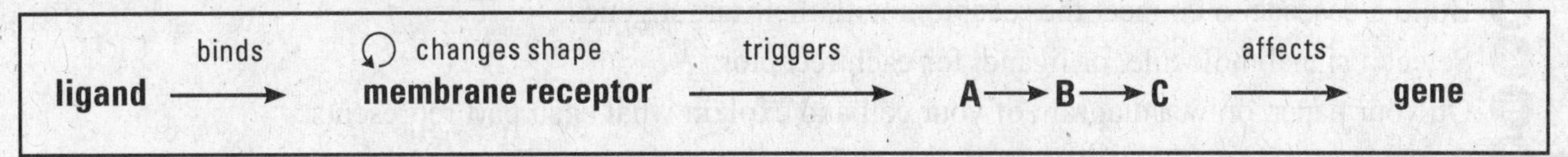

Frizzled is the name of one membrane receptor. It helps control how much B-catenin is present in a cell. B-catenin carries out several functions in a cell. When Frizzled is inactive, any excess B-catenin is broken down very quickly. However, when the Frizzled receptor binds to one of its ligands, it becomes active. The activated Frizzled receptor causes a protein called Dishevelled, in the cytoplasm, to become active. When Dishevelled is active, it stops proteins from breaking down B-catenin. B-catenin then enters the nucleus and turns on many genes, which make proteins.

INTRACELLULAR RECEPTORS

Intracellular receptors are inside the cell. Some intracellular receptors are in the cytoplasm. Others are inside the nucleus. Ligands that can diffuse across the plasma membrane bind to intracellular receptors. These molecules tend to be small and nonpolar. When an intracellular receptor binds to a ligand, the receptor changes shape. This change in shape allows the receptor-ligand complex to interact with nearby molecules in new ways.

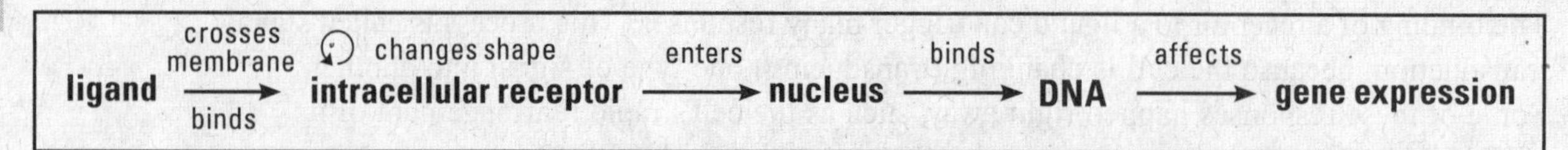

The estrogen receptor is an example of an intracellular receptor. Estrogen is a steroid hormone. Steroid hormones can easily cross plasma membranes. The estrogen receptor is in the nucleus. When it is not bound to estrogen, the estrogen receptor is kept inactive by proteins called chaperones. When the estrogen receptor binds to estrogen, the receptor changes shape. This separates the receptor from the chaperone proteins and allows two receptor-ligand complexes to join together. Once joined, the receptors recognize and bind to specific regions of DNA called estrogen response elements. Based on how the receptors interact with other proteins, binding will turn a gene on or off.

MODELING SIGNAL TRANSDUCTION CASCADES

MATERIALS	large poster paper, tape marker, different colors of paper, dominoes, toy cars

In this activity, you will create a model of a signal transduction cascade. You can use the examples given above or research other examples to create a model of a cell with a membrane receptor and an intracellular receptor. Use the materials listed or other materials that you can think of to demonstrate the domino effect of the signal transduction cascades.

1. Create a cell large enough to contain the transduction cascade. Mark the cell membrane and nuclear membrane. Include at least two "DNA" genes inside the nucleus.
2. Place at least one receptor in the cell membrane and one inside the cell nucleus.
3. Build a cascade to connect the receptors with their target genes.
4. Select a signal molecule, or ligand, for each receptor.
5. On your paper, draw a diagram of your cell and explain what each part represents.
6. Send the signal to each of your receptors and watch the result. Make any adjustments to your cell as necessary.
7. On your paper, explain the results and what those results might mean in a real cell. Explain any limitations of your model.
8. Use your model to demonstrate signal transduction to the rest of your class.

EXPERIMENT WITH OSMOSIS

Pre-AP Activity

In Chapter 3, you have learned that osmosis is the movement of water molecules across a semipermeable membrane from a region of higher concentration to one of lower concentration. You also learned that the terms *isotonic, hypertonic,* and *hypotonic* can be used to describe the concentration of solutions relative to each other.

SOLUTES AND SOLVENTS

Osmosis refers to the movement of water, which is the solvent in many solutions. If you compare two solutions of different concentrations, the solution with a higher solute concentration will have a lower solvent concentration, and vice versa. The direction of osmosis—whether a solution is hypotonic or hypertonic—depends on the relative concentrations of solute particles in the solutions, not the types or variety of solute particles.

WATER BALANCE IN CELLS

The cytoplasm of a cell contains many different solutes: salts, proteins, sugars, and more. In general, the movement of water in and out of a cell is determined by the concentration of particles dissolved in the cytoplasm compared to the concentration of particles dissolved in the fluid surrounding the cell. Cells that have no cell walls are very sensitive to changes in their surroundings. If the surrounding solution becomes hypertonic or hypotonic, the cell will either shrivel up and die or burst and die, respectively. Cells without cell walls must live in an isotonic environment or have adaptations for osmoregulation, the control of water balance.

Cells that have cell walls, such as plants cells, are much more tolerant of changes in their surroundings. In a hypotonic environment, such as when a piece of celery is put into a glass of water, a plant cell swells until its slightly elastic walls reach their limit and begin to exert pressure against the flow of water. This pressure is called turgor pressure, or turgidity, and is the normal state for most plant cells. Turgor pressure allows plant cells to maximize the volume of water they hold and also allows the plant as a whole to achieve its most rigid state, thereby increasing its exposure to sunlight and maximizing its potential for photosynthesis.

Experimenting with Osmosis

In this activity, you will measure the mass of five potato cores and then soak them in solutions of varying concentrations. You will measure their masses the following day and calculate the percent change in mass of each. You will use the data to determine which solutions are hypertonic, hypotonic, and isotonic, and what the concentration of solute is in a potato.

MATERIALS

aluminum foil
table salt (NaCl)
balance or scale
potato
potato corer
distilled water
cups or jars of ~250 mL capacity
100-mL graduated cylinder
knife
marking pen
paper towels

1. Read through steps 2–8 and draw a data table.
2. Label the five cups or jars *Distilled water, 0.5% salt, 1% salt, 5% salt,* and *10% salt.*
3. Place 100 mL of distilled water in the *Distilled water cup,* 99.5 mL in the *0.5% salt cup,* 99 mL in the *1% salt* cup, 95 mL in the *5% salt cup,* and 90 mL in the *10% salt cup.* Add 0.5 grams of table salt to the *0.5% cup,* 1 gram of salt to the *1% cup,* 5 grams to the *5% cup,* and 10 grams to the *10% cup.* Stir each solution until the salt dissolves.
4. Cut five cores from a potato. Trim them so they are approximately the same size. Make sure there is no skin on the potato pieces.
5. Find the mass of each piece of potato. After weighing each piece, record the mass in your data table in the same row as one of the solutions, and then place the piece in that solution.
6. When all the potato pieces are in the solutions, make sure they are completely submerged and then cover each cup with aluminum foil. Let them sit overnight.
7. The next day, remove the potato pieces from the cups, blot them dry with the paper towel, and weigh them. Record the masses in the data table. Feel the potatoes and record their turgidity (how limp or crisp each feels).
8. Calculate and record the percent change in mass for each potato piece. Use plus (+) and minus (–) signs to indicate gain or loss of mass.

Answer the following questions on a separate piece of paper.

1. Describe on a molecular level what happened to the potato piece(s) that gained mass.
2. Describe on a molecular level what happened to the potato piece(s) that lost mass.
3. Did any of the potato pieces not change in mass? If so, explain this on a molecular level.
4. Which of the five solutions were hypotonic to potato cells? Which were hypertonic?
5. What is the approximate concentration of solutes in potato cells? Explain how you know.

Name Period Date

CHAPTER 3 | CELL STRUCTURE AND FUNCTION

Vocabulary Practice

cell theory	vacuole	concentration gradient
cytoplasm	lysosome	osmosis
organelle	centriole	isotonic
prokaryotic cell	cell wall	hypertonic
eukaryotic cell	chloroplast	hypotonic
cytoskeleton	cell membrane	facilitated diffusion
nucleus	phospholipid	active transport
endoplasmic reticulum	fluid mosaic model	endocytosis
ribosome	selective permeability	phagocytosis
Golgi apparatus	receptor	exocytosis
vesicle	passive transport	
mitochondrion	diffusion	

A. Word Origins Circle the Greek and Latin word parts in each vocabulary term. Then use the Greek and Latin meanings to construct a very basic definition of the vocabulary word.

endo-	=	inside	hyper-	=	over, above	chloro-	=	green
exo-	=	outside	hypo-	=	below	iso-	=	equal
phago-	=	eating	lys-	=	loosen	-tonia	=	state of
cyto-	=	cell	-plast	=	small body			

WORD	DEFINITION
1. endocytosis	
2. exocytosis	
3. phagocytosis	
4. hypertonic	
5. hypotonic	
6. isotonic	
7. lysosome	
8. chloroplast	

Name Period Date

WORD	DEFINITION
9. cytoplasm	
10. cytoskeleton	

B. Analogies Read each analogy. Decide which term is most like it.

active transport	exocytosis	passive transport
cell wall	Golgi apparatus	ribosomes
concentration gradient	nucleus	selective permeability

1. Chips in a chocolate chip cookie ____________________

2. Skin of a grape ____________________

3. Allowing only invited guests in to your party ____________________

4. Floating on a raft through a tunnel without paddling ____________________

5. A cab driving you to the party through heavy traffic ____________________

6. Spitting out watermelon seeds ____________________

7. Thick fog in one area, clear in another ____________________

8. An accordion ____________________

9. The chewy center of a candy ____________________

Write your own analogies to show the meaning of these terms:

10. cytoskeleton

____

____

11. phagocytosis

____

____

C. Vector Vocabulary Define the words in the boxes. On the lines across each arrow, write a phrase that describes how the words in the boxes are related to each other.

ACTIVE TRANSPORT

1. ______________________

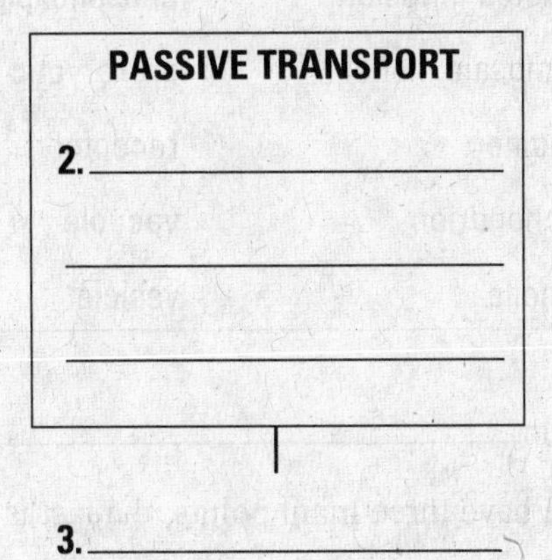

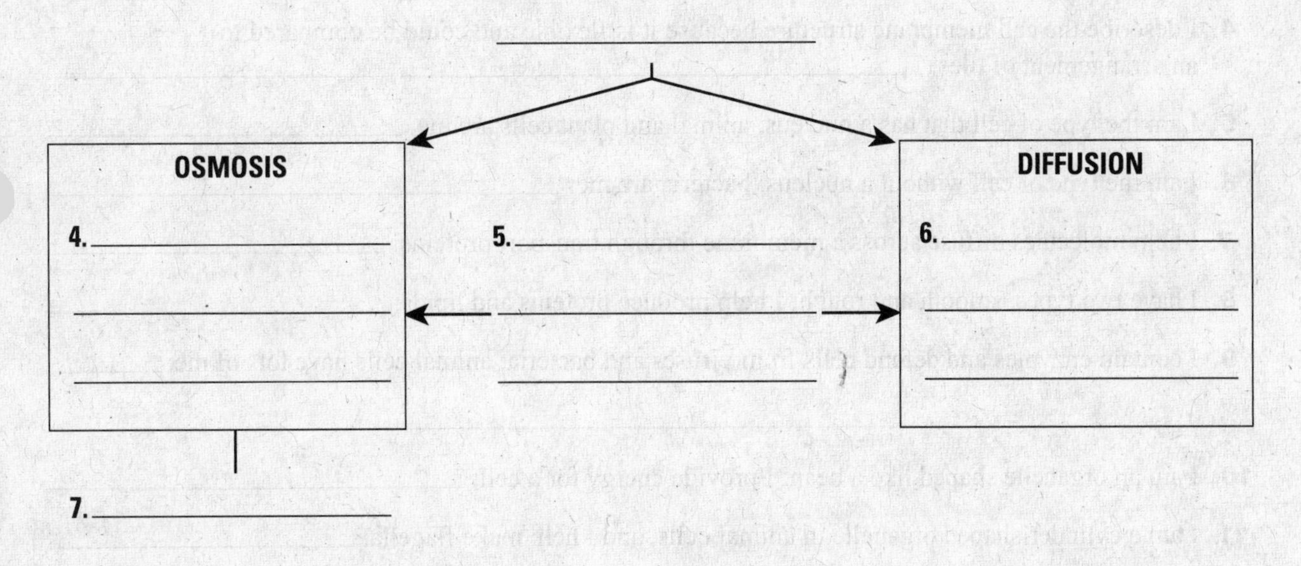

7. ______________________

ISOTONIC

8. ______________________

HYPOTONIC

9. ______________________

HYPERTONIC

10. ______________________

Name Period Date

D. Who Am I? Choose among these terms to answer the riddles below:

cell membrane	facilitated diffusion	phospholipid
cell theory	fluid mosaic model	prokaryotic cell
centriole	lysosome	receptor
endoplasmic reticulum	mitochondrion	vacuole
eukaryotic cell	organelle	vesicle

1. I carry out special jobs in a cell: ______________________

2. I'm an important concept and I have three main points; the last is that all cells come from existing cells: ______________________

3. I make up the two layers of the cell membrane: ______________________

4. I describe the cell membrane structure because it is flexible and could be compared to an arrangement of tiles: ______________________

5. I am the type of cell that has a nucleus; animal and plant cells are me: ______________________

6. I am the type of cell without a nucleus; bacteria are me: ______________________

7. I help molecules diffuse across a membrane through transport proteins: ______________________

8. I have two types, smooth and rough; I help produce proteins and lipids: ______________________

9. I contain enzymes and defend cells from viruses and bacteria; animal cells have lots of me: ______________________

10. I am an organelle shaped like a bean; I provide energy for a cell: ______________________

11. I am a cylinder-shaped organelle in animal cells, and I help make flagella: ______________________

12. I am the outer edge that separates a cell from the outside environment; I control what goes in and out of a cell: ______________________

13. I receive signals from molecules and make sure the right cell gets the right signal at the right time: ______________________

14. I'm a sac filled with fluid inside a cell; I store materials the cell needs: ______________________

15. I'm a little organelle that carries materials from one part of the cell to another; I don't live long, but I can be recycled: ______________________

Name Period Date

SECTION **4.1** CHEMICAL ENERGY AND ATP

Study Guide

KEY CONCEPT
All cells need chemical energy.

VOCABULARY		
ATP	ADP	chemosynthesis

MAIN IDEA: The chemical energy used for most cell processes is carried by ATP.

1. What do all cells use for energy?

____

2. What is ATP?

____

3. What is the relationship between ATP and ADP?

____

____

Fill in the four parts of the cycle diagram below to take notes on the relationship between ATP and ADP.

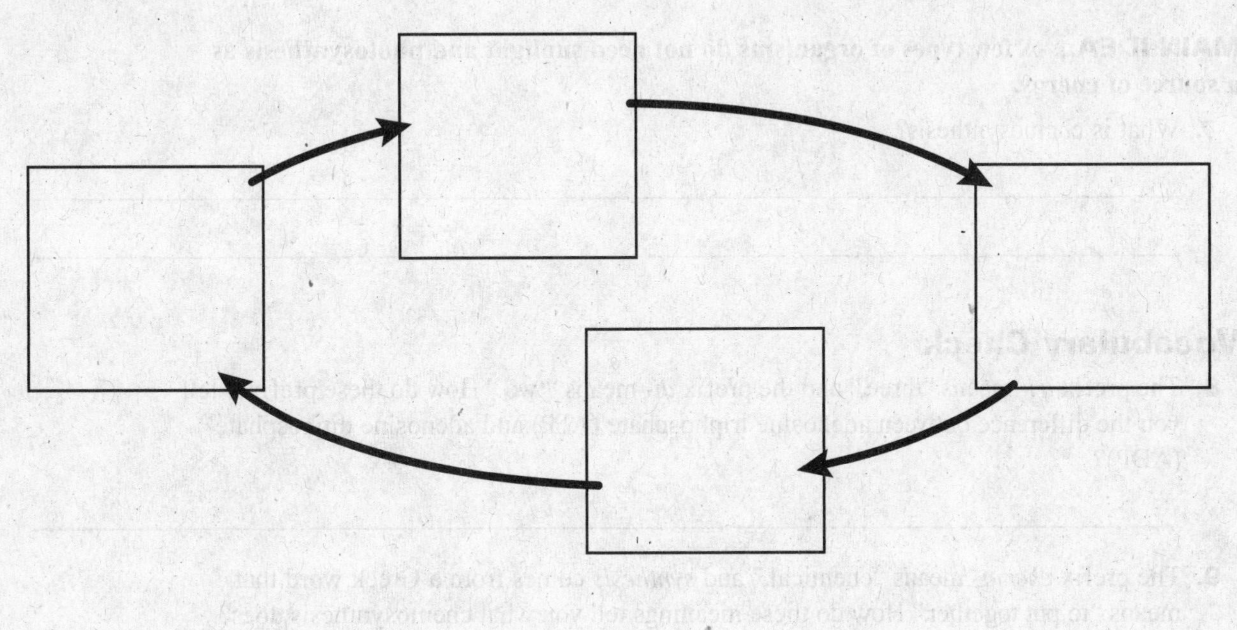

MAIN IDEA: Organisms break down carbon-based molecules to produce ATP.
Use the table below to organize your notes about the different types of molecules that are broken down to make ATP.

Type of Molecule	Role in ATP Production
Carbohydrates	**4.**
Lipids	**5.**
Proteins	**6.**

MAIN IDEA: A few types of organisms do not need sunlight and photosynthesis as a source of energy.

7. What is chemosynthesis?

Vocabulary Check

8. The prefix *tri-* means "three," and the prefix *di-* means "two." How do these prefixes tell you the difference between adenosine triphosphate (ATP) and adenosine diphosphate (ADP)?

9. The prefix *chemo-* means "chemical," and *synthesis* comes from a Greek word that means "to put together." How do these meanings tell you what chemosynthesis does?

Name Period Date

SECTION **4.1** CHEMICAL ENERGY AND ATP

Power Notes

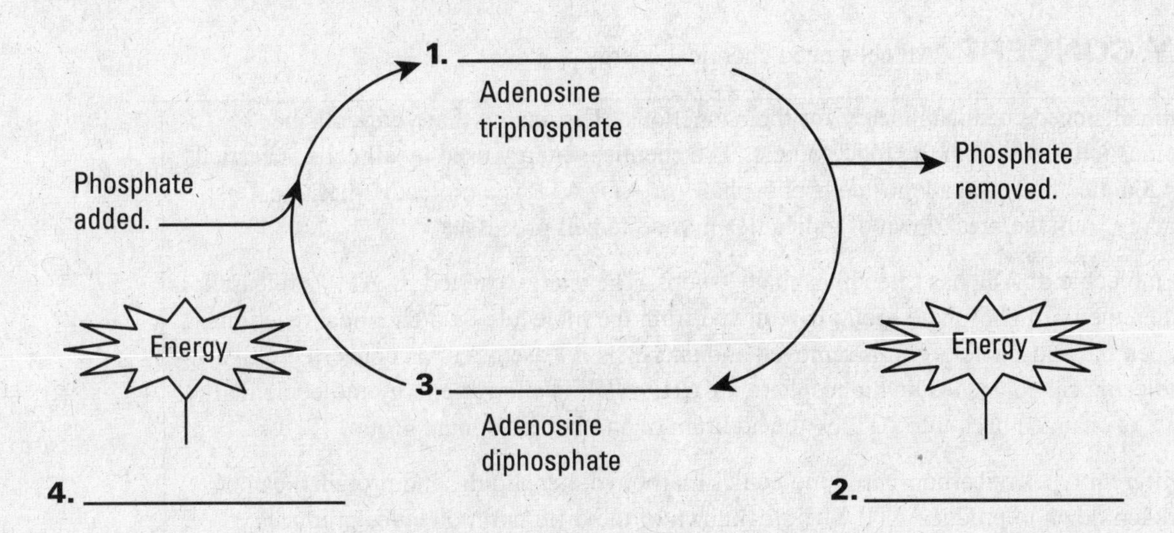

Molecule Type	Energy	Details
5. Carbohydrate		
6. Lipid		
7. Protein		

Chemosynthesis is:

Name Period Date

SECTION **4.1** CHEMICAL ENERGY AND ATP

Reinforcement

KEY CONCEPT All cells need chemical energy.

All cells need chemical energy for their functions. The energy that your cells need comes indirectly from the food you eat. The chemical energy used by all cells is carried by a molecule called adenosine triphosphate, or ATP. **ATP** is a molecule that transfers energy from the breakdown of molecules in food to cell processes.

A molecule of ATP has three phosphate groups. The energy carried by ATP is released when the third phosphate group is removed from the molecule by a chemical reaction. When the phosphate group is removed and energy is released, ATP is converted into a molecule called adenosine diphosphate, or ADP. **ADP** is a lower-energy molecule that can be changed back into ATP by the addition of another phosphate group.

Different types of carbon-based molecules (carbohydrates, lipids, and proteins) can be broken down to produce ATP. The breakdown of the different molecules produces different amounts of ATP. Carbohydrates, especially the simple sugar glucose, are most commonly broken down to make ATP. The breakdown of a lipid produces many more ATP molecules than does the breakdown of a sugar. Proteins are the molecules least likely to be broken down, but they store about the same amount of energy as carbohydrates.

Many organisms must eat other organisms to get the carbon-based molecules they need to make ATP. Some organisms, such as plants, use a process called photosynthesis to make their own food molecules. Other organisms that survive without light can make their own food molecules through a process called **chemosynthesis.**

1. What is the function of ATP?

____

____

2. What is ADP?

____

____

3. Which types of carbon-based molecules can be broken down to make ATP?

____

Name Period Date

SECTION
4.2

OVERVIEW OF PHOTOSYNTHESIS

Study Guide

KEY CONCEPT

The overall process of photosynthesis produces sugars that store chemical energy.

VOCABULARY	
photosynthesis	light-dependent reactions
chlorophyll	light-independent reactions
thylakoid	

MAIN IDEA: Photosynthetic organisms are producers.

1. Why are some organisms called producers?

____

2. What is the function of photosynthesis?

____

3. What is chlorophyll?

____

MAIN IDEA: Photosynthesis in plants occurs in chloroplasts.

4. What are chloroplasts?

____

5. In which two parts of a chloroplast does photosynthesis take place?

____

6. What are thylakoids?

____

7. Write the chemical equation for the overall process of photosynthesis. Then explain what the equation means and identify the reactants, products, and the meaning of the several arrows.

____

____

____

8. What are the differences between the light-dependent reactions and the light-independent reactions?

____

____

CHAPTER 4
Cells and Energy

Use the space below to sketch and label a chloroplast. On the sketch, write the four steps of the photosynthesis process.

Photosynthesis

Vocabulary Check

9. The prefix *photo-* means "light," and *synthesis* means "to put together." How do those meanings tell you what happens during photosynthesis?

10. The prefix *chloro-* means "green," and the suffix *-phyll* means "leaf." How are these meanings related to chlorophyll?

11. The prefix *in-* means "not." How does this meaning tell you which reactions in photosynthesis require light, and which reactions do not?

Name Period Date

SECTION **4.2** OVERVIEW OF PHOTOSYNTHESIS

Power Notes

Photosynthesis:

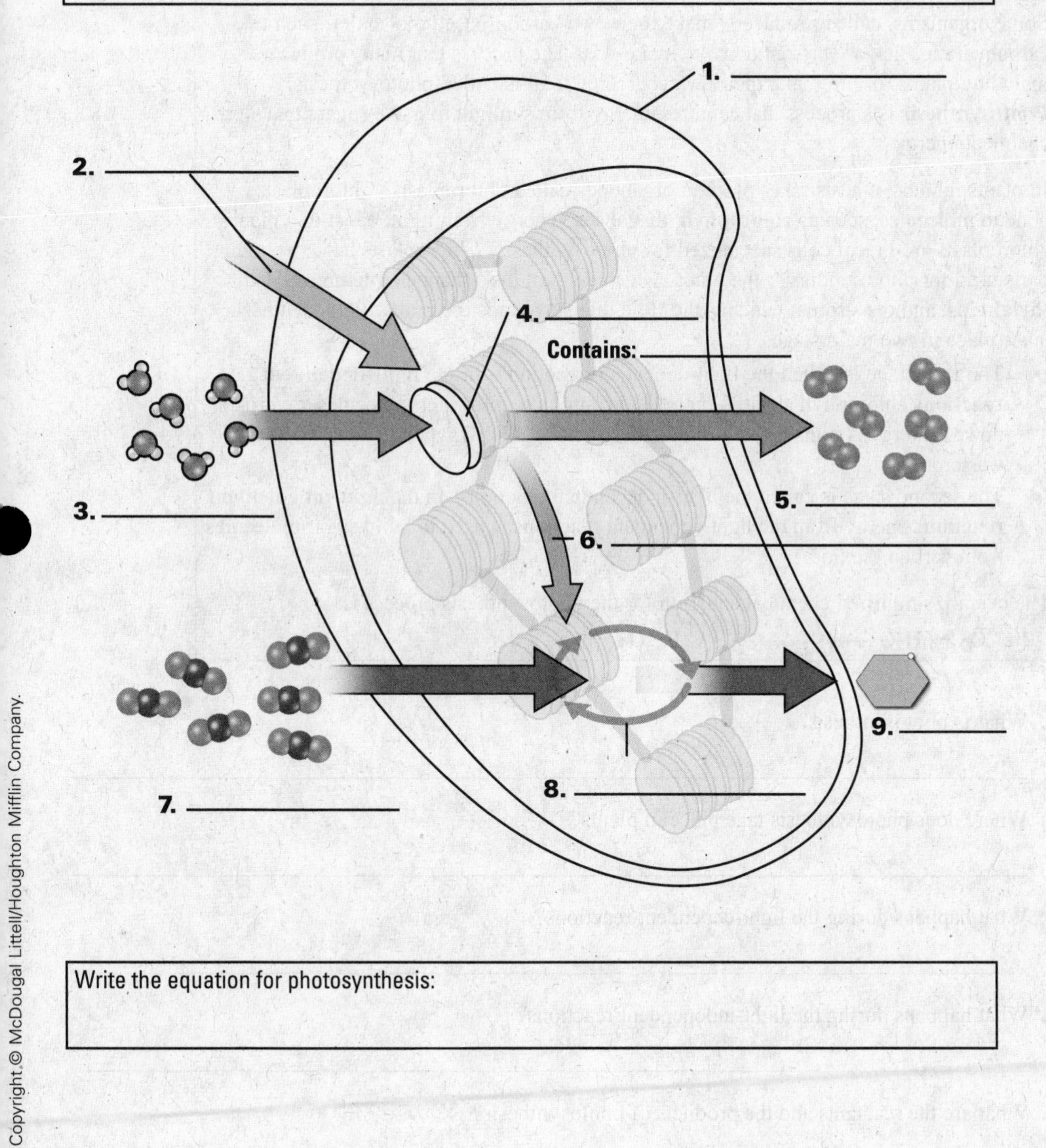

Write the equation for photosynthesis:

CHAPTER 4 Cells and Energy

Name Period Date

SECTION **4.2** OVERVIEW OF PHOTOSYNTHESIS

Reinforcement

KEY CONCEPT The overall process of photosynthesis produces sugars that store chemical energy.

Some organisms, called producers, make their own carbon-based molecules, such as carbohydrates, that are broken down to make ATP. The process that many producers, including plants, use to make their own source of food is called photosynthesis. **Photosynthesis** is a process that captures energy from sunlight to make sugars that store chemical energy.

In plants, photosynthesis takes place in organelles called chloroplasts. Chloroplasts contain molecules, such as **chlorophyll,** that absorb energy from light. Most of a plant's chloroplasts are in leaf cells specialized for photosynthesis. Chloroplasts have two main parts used for photosynthesis: the grana, which contain disk-shaped structures called **thylakoids,** and the stroma, which is the fluid that surrounds the grana. Photosynthesis takes place in two main stages.

- The first stage is called the light-dependent reactions. In the **light-dependent reactions** chlorophyll absorbs energy from sunlight and water molecules are broken down. Energy is transferred to molecules such as ATP. Oxygen is released as a waste product.
- The second stage is called the light-independent reactions. In the **light-independent reactions** energy from the light-dependent reactions is used to build sugar molecules from carbon dioxide.

The overall, simplified chemical equation for the photosynthesis process is:

$$6CO_2 + 6H_2O \rightarrow\rightarrow\rightarrow\rightarrow\rightarrow\rightarrow\rightarrow C_6H_{12}O_6 + 6O_2$$

1. What is photosynthesis?

____

2. Where does photosynthesis take place in plants?

____

3. What happens during the light-dependent reactions?

____

4. What happens during the light-independent reactions?

____

5. What are the reactants and the products of photosynthesis?

____

Name Period Date

SECTION
4.3 | PHOTOSYNTHESIS IN DETAIL
Study Guide

KEY CONCEPT
Photosynthesis requires a series of chemical reactions.

VOCABULARY	
photosystem	ATP synthase
electron transport chain	Calvin cycle

MAIN IDEA: The first stage of photosynthesis captures and transfers energy.

1. Overall, what is the function of the light-dependent reactions?

2. What are photosystems?

3. Which molecules carry energy to the light-independent reactions?

Fill in the sequence diagram below to follow the seven steps of the light-dependent reactions.

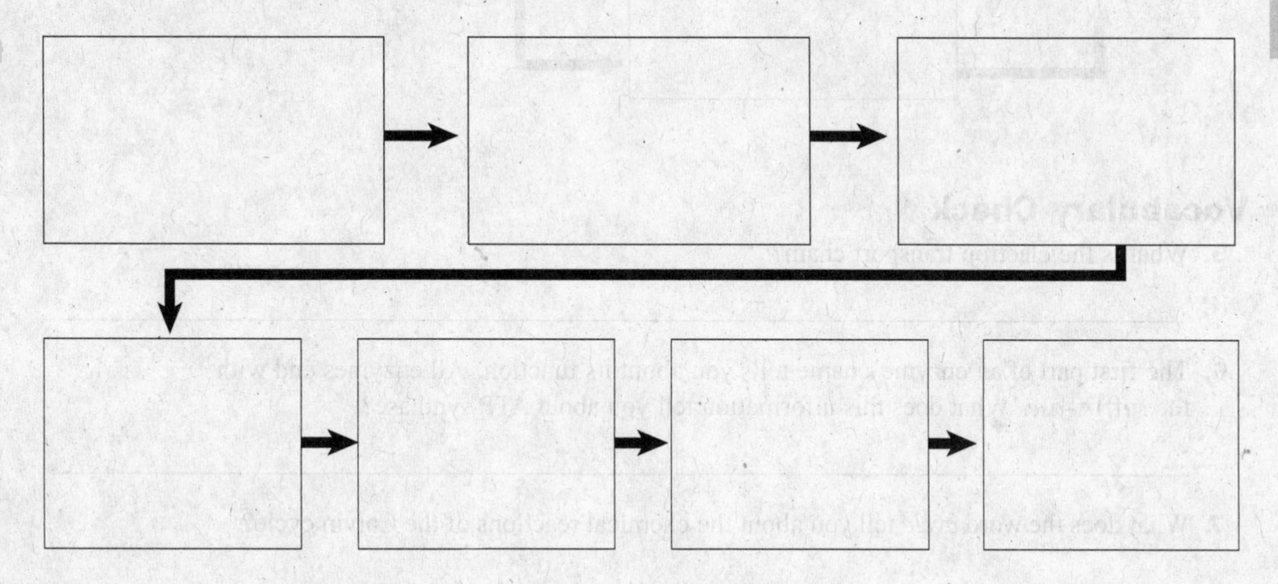

Name Period Date

MAIN IDEA: The second stage of photosynthesis uses energy from the first stage to make sugars.

4. What is the function of the Calvin cycle?

Fill in the cycle diagram to summarize the four steps of the Calvin cycle.

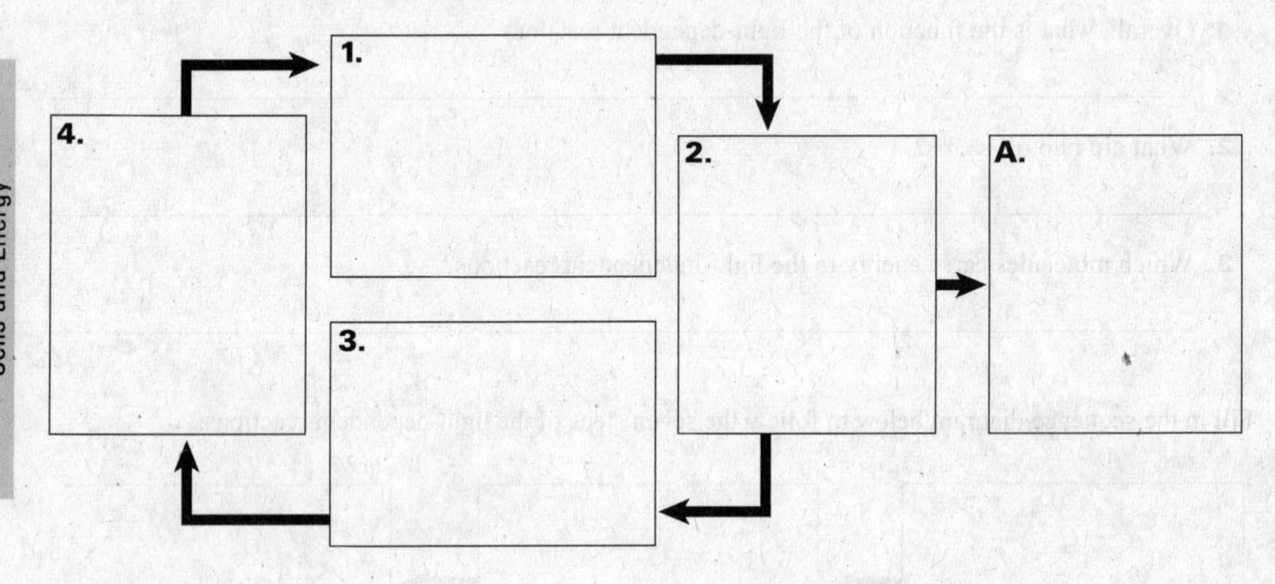

Vocabulary Check

5. What is the electron transport chain?

6. The first part of an enzyme's name tells you about its function. All enzymes end with the suffix *-ase.* What does this information tell you about ATP synthase?

7. What does the word *cycle* tell you about the chemical reactions of the Calvin cycle?

Name Period Date

SECTION **4.3** | PHOTOSYNTHESIS IN DETAIL

Power Notes

Light-Dependent Reactions

Step	Description
1	
2	
3	
4	
5	
6	
7	

Light-Independent Reactions

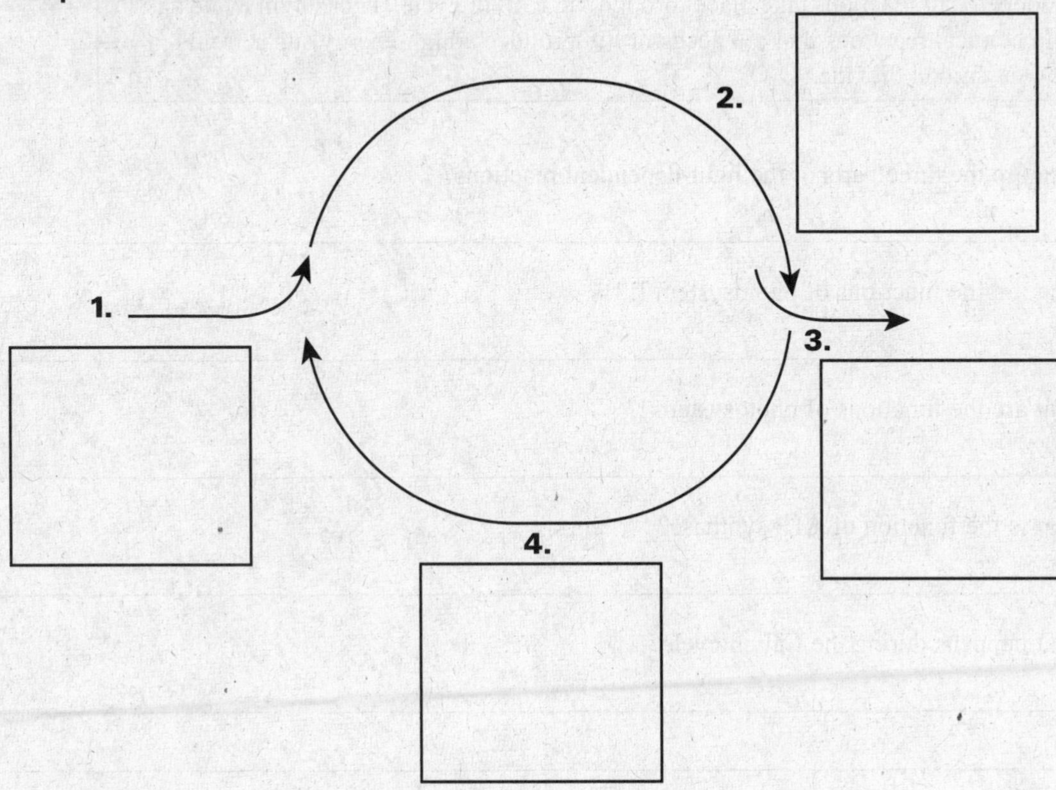

Name Period Date

SECTION 4.3 | PHOTOSYNTHESIS IN DETAIL

Reinforcement

KEY CONCEPT Photosynthesis requires a series of chemical reactions.

Photosynthesis takes place in two main stages: the light-dependent reactions and the light-independent reactions. The light-dependent reactions capture and transfer energy. The light-dependent reactions mainly take place in the thylakoid membranes through two groups of molecules, called **photosystems.**

- Photosystem II: In photosystem II, chlorophyll and other light-absorbing molecules capture energy from sunlight. The energy is transferred to electrons that travel through a series of proteins in the thylakoid membrane called an **electron transport chain.** Water molecules are broken down. Hydrogen ions from the water molecules are pumped across the thylakoid membrane.
- Photosystem I: Additional energy is absorbed from sunlight and transferred to electrons in the electron transport chain. The electrons are used to produce a molecule called NADPH, which carries energy to the light-independent reactions.
- ATP synthase: Hydrogen ions flow through a complex enzyme called **ATP synthase** that produces ATP molecules that are transferred to the light-independent reactions.

The light-independent reactions use the ATP and NADPH from the light-dependent reactions, and carbon dioxide from the atmosphere, to make sugars. The light-independent reactions take place through the **Calvin cycle.** The Calvin cycle has several chemical reactions that are necessary to produce a high-energy sugar from low-energy carbon dioxide.

1. What are the three parts of the light-dependent reactions?

____

2. What are the functions of photosystem II?

____

3. What are the functions of photosystem I?

____

4. What is the function of ATP synthase?

____

5. What happens during the Calvin cycle?

____

____

Name Period Date

SECTION 4.4 | OVERVIEW OF CELLULAR RESPIRATION

Study Guide

KEY CONCEPT

The overall process of cellular respiration converts sugar into ATP using oxygen.

VOCABULARY	
cellular respiration	anaerobic
aerobic	Krebs cycle
glycolysis	

MAIN IDEA: Cellular respiration makes ATP by breaking down sugars.

1. What is cellular respiration?

____

2. Why is cellular respiration called an aerobic process?

____

3. Where does cellular respiration take place?

____

4. What happens during glycolysis?

____

MAIN IDEA: Cellular respiration is like a mirror image of photosynthesis.

5. In what two ways does cellular respiration seem to be the opposite of photosynthesis?

____

____

6. In which two parts of a mitochondrion does cellular respiration take place?

____

7. Write the chemical equation for the overall process of cellular respiration.

____

8. Explain what the equation means. Identify the reactants, products, and the meaning of the several arrows.

____

____

____

CHAPTER 4 Cells and Energy

Name Period Date

Use the space below to sketch and label a mitochondrion. On the sketch, write the four steps of the cellular respiration process that occur in the mitochondrion.

Cellular Respiration

Vocabulary Check

9. The prefix *glyco-* comes from a Greek word that means "sweet." The suffix *-lysis* comes from a Greek word that means "to loosen." How are the meanings of these word parts related to the meaning of *glycolysis*?

10. What does it mean to say that glycolysis is an anaerobic process?

11. What is the Krebs cycle?

Name Period Date

SECTION **4.4** OVERVIEW OF CELLULAR RESPIRATION

Power Notes

Cellular respiration:

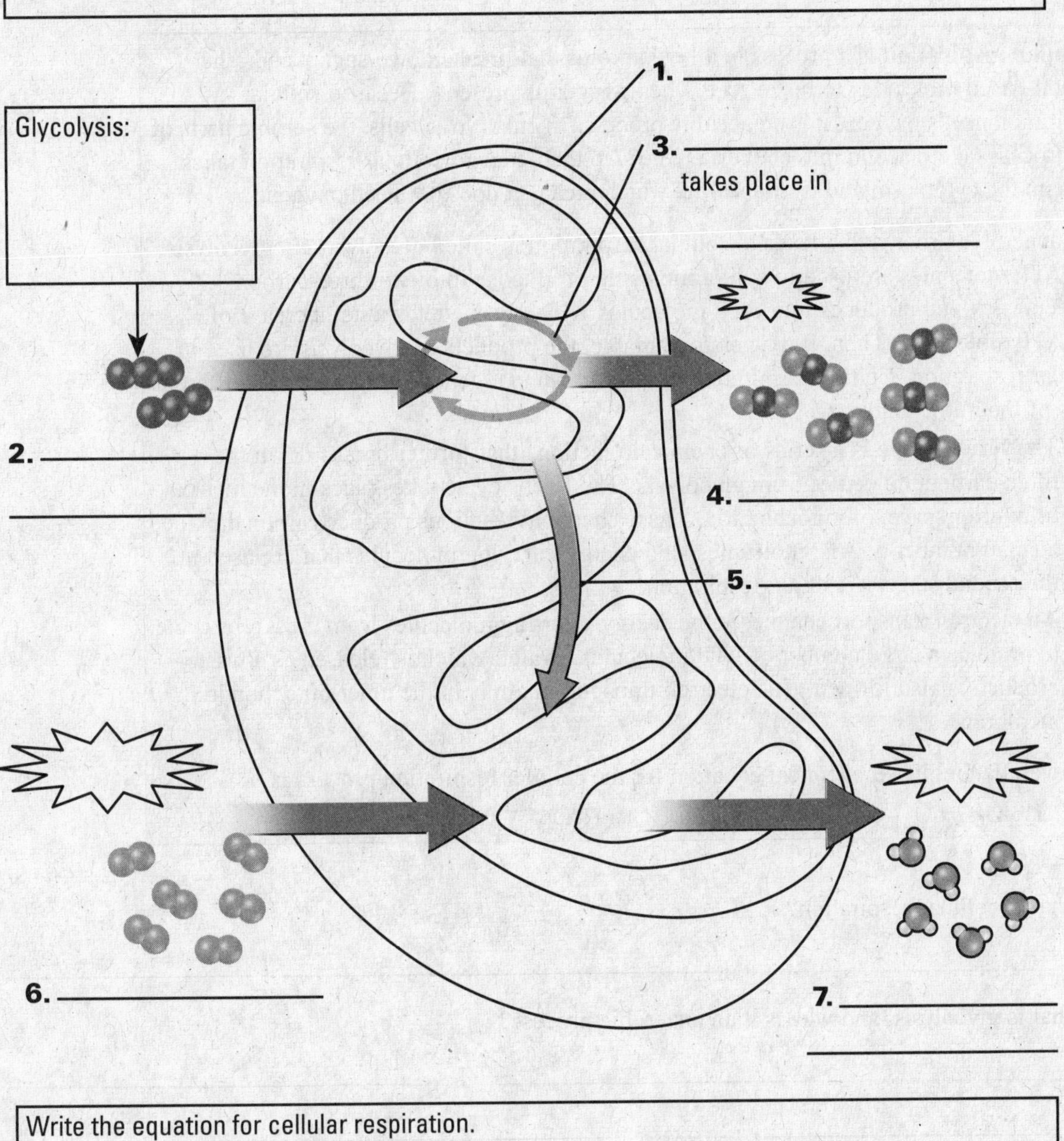

Write the equation for cellular respiration.

Name Period Date

SECTION **4.4** OVERVIEW OF CELLULAR RESPIRATION

Reinforcement

KEY CONCEPT The overall process of cellular respiration converts sugar into ATP using oxygen.

Cellular respiration is a process in all eukaryotes that breaks down sugars and other carbon-based molecules to make ATP when oxygen is present. Because cellular respiration needs oxygen, it is an **aerobic** process. In eukaryotic cells, the aerobic parts of the process take place in mitochondria. The step that leads to cellular respiration takes place in the cytoplasm and is **anaerobic,** which means it does not need oxygen.

The anaerobic process that leads to cellular respiration is called glycolysis. In **glycolysis,** two ATP molecules are used to split a molecule of glucose into two three-carbon molecules, which produces four ATP molecules. Glycolysis yields a net increase of two ATP molecules. Then, if oxygen is available, the products of glycolysis are used in cellular respiration. Cellular respiration takes place in two general stages, in two different parts of the mitochondria.

- The **Krebs cycle** is a series of chemical reactions that further breaks down the three-carbon molecules from glycolysis. The Krebs cycle takes place in the matrix, or interior space, of mitochondria. These chemical reactions produce carbon dioxide, a small number of ATP molecules, and energy-carrying molecules that are used in the second stage of cellular respiration.
- An electron transport chain uses the energy-carrying molecules from the Krebs cycle to produce a large number of ATP molecules. Water, which is released as a waste product, is also formed. The electron transport chain is in the inner mitochondrial membrane.

The overall, simplified chemical equation for the cellular respiration process is

$$C_6H_{12}O_6 + 6O_2 \rightarrow\rightarrow\rightarrow\rightarrow\rightarrow\rightarrow\rightarrow 6CO_2 + 6H_2O$$

1. What is cellular respiration?

____

2. What is glycolysis, and why is it an anaerobic process?

____

____

3. What happens in the Krebs cycle?

____

____

4. What is the function of the electron transport chain?

____

CHAPTER 4
Cells and Energy

Name Period Date

SECTION **4.5** CELLULAR RESPIRATION IN DETAIL

Study Guide

KEY CONCEPT

Cellular respiration is an aerobic process with two main stages.

MAIN IDEA: Glycolysis is needed for cellular respiration.

1. What is the function of glycolysis?

____

2. What happens to the molecules formed during glycolysis when oxygen is available?

____

3. What is meant by a "net gain of two ATP molecules" from glycolysis?

____

MAIN IDEA: The Krebs cycle is the first main part of cellular respiration.

4. What is the function of the Krebs cycle?

____

Complete the cycle diagram below to summarize the six steps of the Krebs cycle.

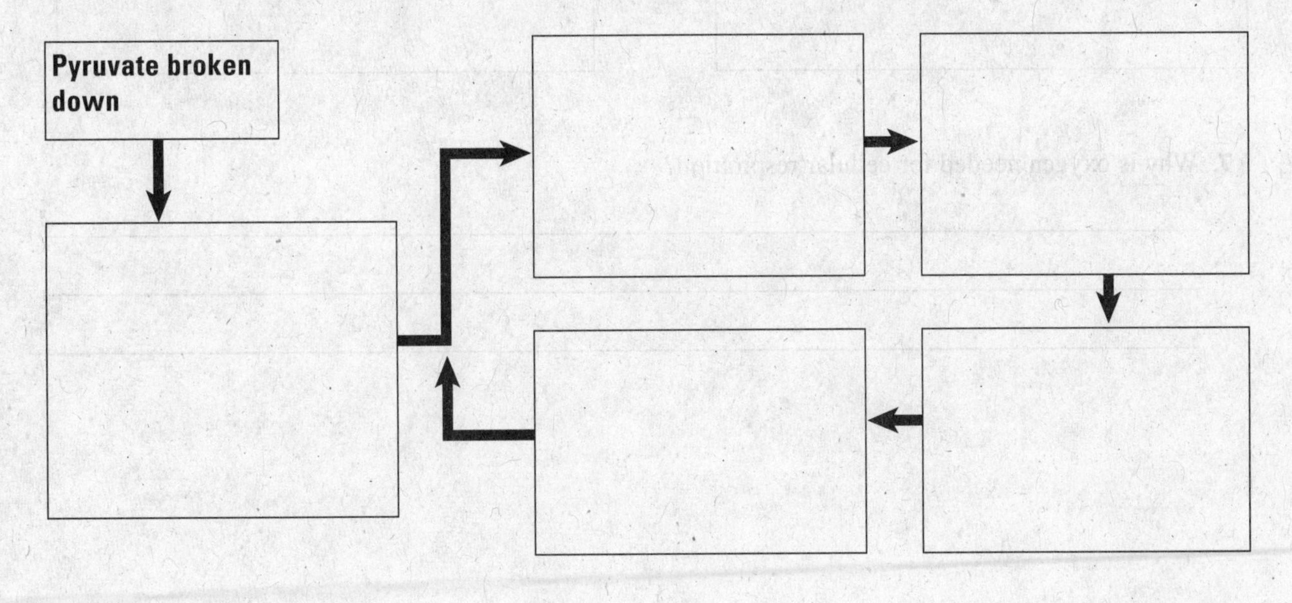

CHAPTER 4 Cells and Energy

Name Period Date

MAIN IDEA: The electron transport chain is the second main part of cellular respiration.

5. Where is the electron transport chain in cellular respiration located?

____

6. What is the function of the electron transport chain?

____

Fill in the sequence below to take notes on the four steps of the electron transport chain.

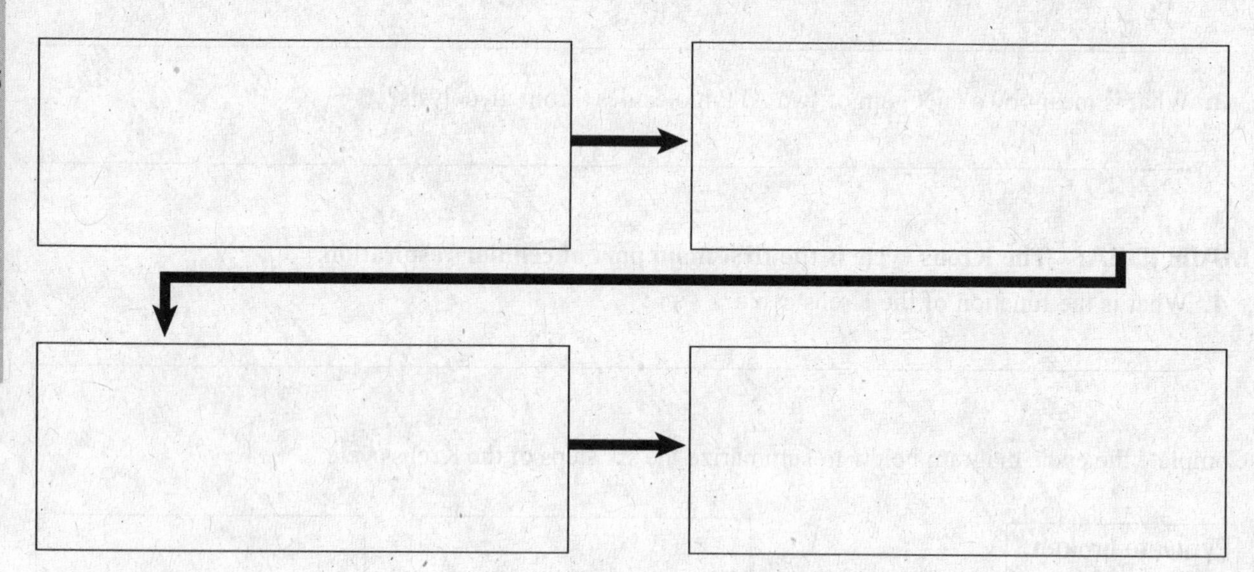

7. Why is oxygen needed for cellular respiration?

____

____

____

Name Period Date

SECTION 4.5 | CELLULAR RESPIRATION IN DETAIL

Power Notes

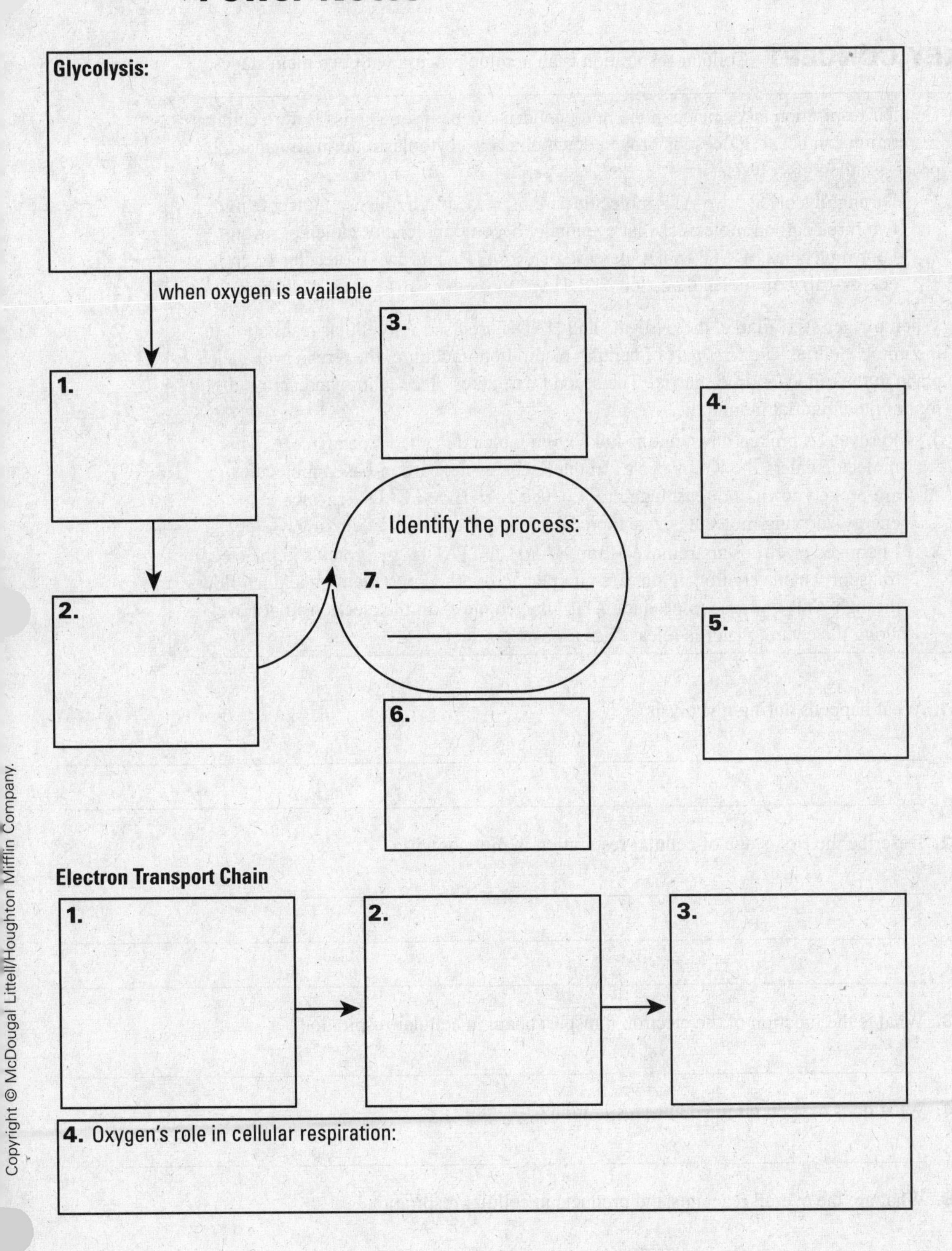

CHAPTER 4 Cells and Energy

Name Period Date

SECTION **4.5** | CELLULAR RESPIRATION IN DETAIL

Reinforcement

KEY CONCEPT Cellular respiration is an aerobic process with two main stages.

Cellular respiration takes place in the mitochondria of eukaryotic cells. Before cellular respiration can occur, glucose is broken down in a cell's cytoplasm during an anaerobic process called glycolysis.

- During glycolysis, two ATP molecules are used to split a glucose molecule into two three-carbon molecules that eventually become molecules called pyruvate. Four molecules of ATP (a net increase of two ATP), and two molecules of an energy-carrying molecule called NADH are formed.

When oxygen is available, the pyruvate and NADH are used for cellular respiration in the mitochondria. The first part of cellular respiration, including the Krebs cycle, takes place in the mitochondrial matrix. The second part takes place within and across the inner mitochondrial membrane.

1. Pyruvate is broken down and is linked to a molecule called Coenzyme A. This molecule enters the Krebs cycle. In the Krebs cycle, carbon-based molecules are broken down and rearranged to produce NADH and $FADH_2$, which are energy-carrying molecules, two molecules of ATP, and carbon dioxide waste.
2. Energized electrons are removed from NADH and $FADH_2$ by proteins in the electron transport chain. Hydrogen ions are pumped across the inner membrane, then flow through ATP synthase to produce ATP. Oxygen picks up the electrons that travel along the chain. Water is released as a waste product.

1. What happens during glycolysis?

____

____

2. Describe the first stage of cellular respiration in mitochondria.

____

____

____

3. What is the function of the electron transport chain in cellular respiration?

____

4. What does oxygen do in cellular respiration?

____

5. What are the overall reactants and products in cellular respiration?

____

Name Period Date

SECTION **4.6** FERMENTATION

Study Guide

KEY CONCEPT

Fermentation allows the production of a small amount of ATP without oxygen.

VOCABULARY
fermentation
lactic acid

MAIN IDEA: Fermentation allows glycolysis to continue.

1. What is the importance of fermentation?

2. What is the function of fermentation?

3. When does fermentation take place in your muscle cells?

4. Why is fermentation an anaerobic process?

5. How is fermentation involved in the production of ATP?

In the space below, show and label the process of lactic acid fermentation.

Lactic Acid Fermentation

CHAPTER 4 Cells and Energy

MAIN IDEA: Fermentation and its products are important in several ways.
In the space below, show and label the process of alcoholic fermentation.

Alcoholic Fermentation

6. How are lactic acid fermentation and alcoholic fermentation similar? different?

7. Name one commercial use of lactic acid fermentation.

8. Name one commercial use of alcoholic fermentation.

Vocabulary Check

9. The term *fermentation* is based on a word that means "to bubble." How is this meaning related to your understanding of the fermentation process?

10. What is lactic acid?

Name Period Date

SECTION 4.6 | FERMENTATION

Power Notes

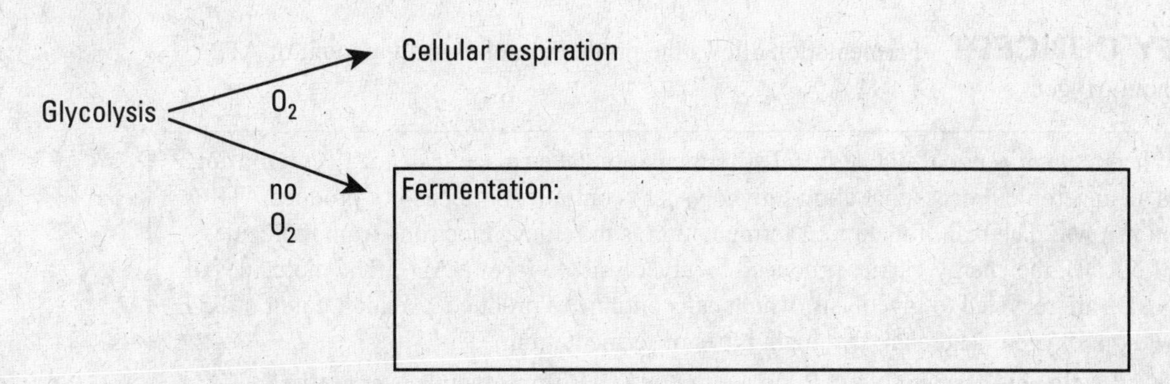

Lactic Acid Fermentation

Process:

Alcoholic Fermentation

Process:

Uses of Fermentation

1.

2.

3.

Name Period Date

SECTION **4.6** FERMENTATION

Reinforcement

KEY CONCEPT Fermentation allows the production of a small amount of ATP without oxygen.

When oxygen is not available in cells, fermentation takes place instead. **Fermentation** is an anaerobic process that allows glycolysis to continue, but does not produce ATP on its own. The main function of fermentation is to remove electrons from molecules of NADH, the energy-carrier produced by glycolysis, to form NAD^+. The molecules of NAD^+ are recycled to glycolysis, which can continue to produce a small amount of ATP without oxygen. There are two main types of fermentation.

- Lactic acid fermentation: Pyruvate and NADH from glycolysis enter the fermentation process. Energy from the NADH molecules is used to convert pyruvate into lactic acid. NADH molecules are converted into NAD^+ molecules that are recycled to glycolysis to pick up more electrons. This type of fermentation occurs in many types of cells, including human muscle cells.
- Alcoholic fermentation: Like lactic acid fermentation, pyruvate and NADH from glycolysis enter fermentation. Energy from NADH is used to break down pyruvate into an alcohol and carbon dioxide. NADH molecules are converted into NAD^+ molecules that are recycled to glycolysis. Alcoholic fermentation is used by many types of yeast.

Both types of fermentation are used in various commercial processes. Lactic acid fermentation is used to make yogurt. Alcoholic fermentation is used to make dough rise.

1. What is the function of fermentation?

____

____

____

2. How are lactic acid fermentation and alcoholic fermentation similar? different?

____

____

____

____

3. How is fermentation used in commercial processes?

____

Name Period Date

CHAPTER 4 | INTERPRETING GRAPHS

Data Analysis Practice

Scientists use data tables to organize their experimental data. Often, the data are graphed because a graph can make the data easier to interpret. Graphs quickly show a relationship between two variables.

Scientists exposed two groups of seedlings to various amounts of light. One group was exposed to low light conditions (LL) and the other group was exposed to moderate light (ML) conditions. Scientists measured the amount of chlorophyll in the seedlings at regular intervals during a 48-hour period. The amount of chlorophyll in the seedlings is expressed in micrograms of chlorophyll per gram of seedling (μg/g). The data from both groups are shown in the graph below.

GRAPH 1. AMOUNT OF CHLOROPHYLL WITH DIFFERENT AMOUNTS OF LIGHT

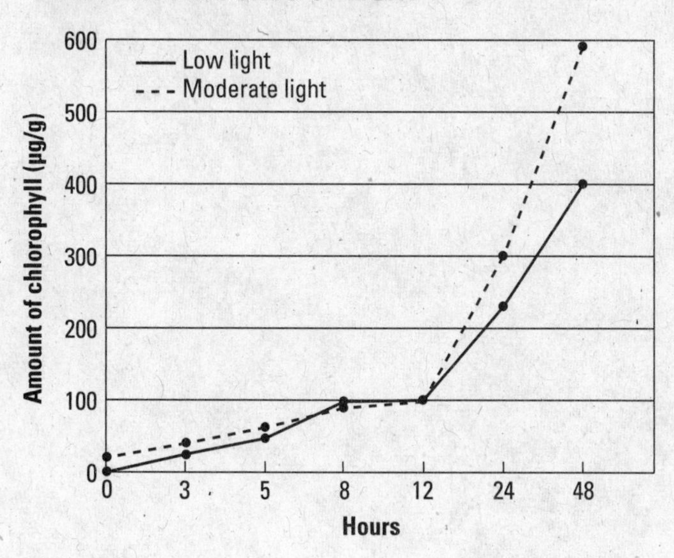

1. **Analyze** Approximately how much chlorophyll was present in the low-light plants after 24 hours? In the moderate-light plants after 24 hours?

2. **Conclude** What are the similarities and differences between the low-light seedlings and the moderate-light seedlings?

Name Period Date

3. Infer To which of the two lighting conditions would you expose seedlings if you wanted to maximize the rate of photosynthesis in the plants? Why?

___

___

___

Name Period Date

CHAPTER 4 | LEAF STRUCTURE: BUILT FOR PHOTOSYNTHESIS

Pre-AP Activity

You know that structure and function are related in biology. In Chapter 4 you have learned how the structure of chloroplasts enables a plant to capture the Sun's energy, then convert and store it as chemical energy, in a process called photosynthesis. This demonstrates the structure-function relationship at a cellular level. The structure–function relationship doesn't stop there. The cells in which photosynthesis is carried out are further specialized into different tissues that are structured in such a way as to ensure that

- the raw materials needed for photosynthesis—sunlight, water vapor, carbon dioxide—are supplied to the chloroplasts
- the energy-rich product—sugar—is delivered to the rest of the plant
- the unused byproduct—oxygen—is removed

Collectively these cells and tissues form an organ—the leaf—that is well suited to photosynthesis.

CELLS AND TISSUES

The diagram below shows the cross section of a leaf. Individual cells are shown in outline; the tiny dark ovals are chloroplasts. Use the descriptions of plant cells and tissues that follow to identify the components. Include labels for the *epidermis, guard cells, stoma, palisade mesophyll, spongy mesophyll,* and *vascular bundle.*

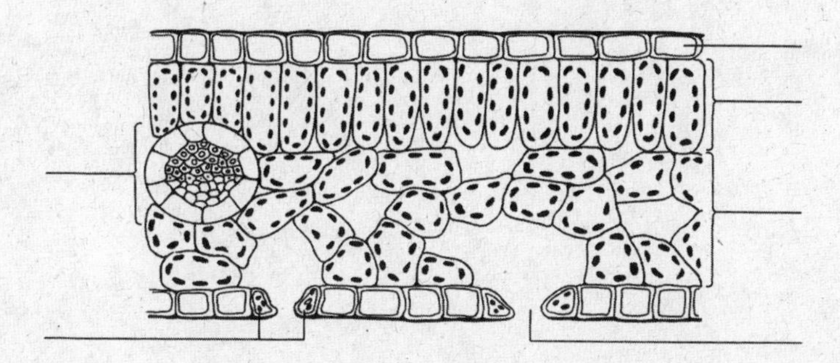

Epidermal Tissue The cells of the *epidermis* cover every surface of a leaf exposed to air. The cells mostly lack chloroplasts and so are colorless. The cell walls of epidermal tissue contain cutin, an insoluble lipid polymer that feels waxy to the touch. Typically found in the lower surface of the epidermis are specialized pairs of guard cells, which do contain chloroplasts. Together the *guard cells* form a structure called a *stoma* (*plural,* stomata) that opens and closes in response to the availability of water.

Mesophyll Tissue The cells that make up this tissue contain large numbers of chloroplasts. *Palisade mesophyll* is made up of elongated rectangular cells that pack tightly together. *Spongy mesophyll* is made up of cells that are irregular in shape and so less compact.

Name Period Date

Vascular Tissue The cells that make up a *vascular bundle* are tubelike cells that stack end to end. Cells of the xylem move water and dissolved nutrients from the roots into the upper parts of a plant. Cells of the phloem carry sugars away from the leaves into lower parts of a plant.

Having read the descriptions and labeled the diagram, answer the following questions on a separate piece of paper. For questions 4 and 5, you might first want to examine a tree to note the general shape, size, thickness, and orientation of its leaves.

1. Write a word equation to identify the reactants and products of photosynthesis.
2. Identify three important functions of the epidermis that support the photosynthetic process. Describe in what way the cells of the epidermis are suited to these functions.
3. Together the mesophyll tissues form the ground tissue of a leaf, where most photosynthetic activity occurs. Considering the shape and position of the cells of the tissues, describe how the two tissues work together to ensure that a leaf produces nutrients sufficient to keep a plant alive.
4. The vascular bundles form the veins of a leaf. From your own observations, what seems to be the optimal position of vascular bundles?
5. From your own observations, what seems to be the optimal position of leaves on a tree?
6. What mechanism has produced the adaptations necessary for photosynthesis seen in a leaf?

Name Period Date

CHAPTER 4 | ORDER VERSUS DISORDER IN LIVING MATTER

Pre-AP Activity

In Chapter 1, you learned that one of the characteristics of life is that it needs a constant supply of energy to maintain itself. As you have learned in Chapter 4, photosynthesis is the primary means by which energy is brought into the biosphere and cellular respiration is one of just a few ways in which it can be released.

ENERGY

In physics, energy is typically defined as "the capacity to do work." It comes in different forms. Mechanical and electrical energy, as well as heat and light, are forms of kinetic energy—energy associated with the motion of an object. Potential energy is energy associated with an object's position. Gravity represents a source of potential energy, as does the energy stored in chemical bonds. As an object does work, energy is often changed from one form to another. In biology, an organism does work when it interacts with the environment, but a large amount of work is also done to keep an organism growing and its living matter organized. When an organism "works," its cells transform energy.

THERMODYNAMICS

Thermodynamics is the study of energy transformations. Any collection of matter that is being studied is referred to as a system, whether that system is the universe or an organism. There are two types of systems, open and closed. In a closed system, matter and energy are not exchanged with the surroundings; in an open system, matter and energy are exchanged with the surroundings.

Two laws of thermodynamics govern energy transformations.

- The first law of thermodynamics, also known as the law of conservation of energy, states that energy can be transferred or transformed, but it cannot be created or destroyed.
- The second law of thermodynamics states that not all of the energy that is transferred or transformed can be used for work; some of it is wasted.

Wasted energy increases the overall disorder in the universe (the system and its surroundings). Organisms typically release a lot of wasted energy in the form of heat. Heat is generated when molecules move and collide in a disorganized manner, and it is this form of energy that is released following chemical reactions. Entropy is a quantity that measures the amount of disorder. According to the second law, every time energy is transferred or transformed in a spontaneous process, the amount of entropy (disorder) in the universe increases.

1. The universe is a closed system that encompasses all matter and energy. How is it that energy can be considered wasted in a system that encompasses all energy?

____

____

2. How would you describe the measure of entropy in an organism?

____

____

3. How is it possible for energy transformations to increase the order in living things if, according to the second law of thermodynamics, energy transformations make the universe more disordered?

4. If you could view the history of Earth as you might a video set to fast forward, you would see a planet that was barren and devoid of life change to one where organisms of every sort occupy just about every square inch of its surface. How is it that there is always more energy available to support a steady increase in highly organized living matter despite the fact that so much energy is used as well as wasted by life cycles?

5. Producers, such as plants, capture energy from the Sun and store it in energy-rich compounds that animals use as a source of energy. Animals that feed on plants directly are primary consumers, animals that feed on primary consumers are secondary consumers, and so it goes as the energy captured by plants or other producers moves up a food chain. These feeding relationships are often depicted in an energy pyramid, with producers at the base. How does the structure and shape of an energy pyramid support the idea that energy is being lost through living matter?

6. Heat is a form of kinetic energy that increases the motion of particles and therefore increases the opportunity for chemical reactions to occur. Your body maintains a stable internal environment by keeping its internal temperature at about 98.6 °F. Yet your cells do not use heat to do work but radiate the heat out of your body, into your surroundings. Instead your body uses molecules such as ATP and enzymes to do the body's work. Why doesn't the body use the heat available to it as a source of energy?

Name Period Date

CHAPTER 4 | CELLS AND ENERGY

Vocabulary Practice

ATP	light-independent reactions	glycolysis
ADP	photosystem	anaerobic
chemosynthesis	electron transport chain	Krebs cycle
photosynthesis	ATP synthase	fermentation
chlorophyll	Calvin cycle	lactic acid
thylakoid	cellular respiration	
light-dependent reactions	aerobic	

A. Matching Write the vocabulary term or phrase next to its definition.

Calvin cycle	electron transport chain	photosystem
chlorophyll	light-dependent reaction	thylakoid

_______________ **1.** Coin-shaped compartment that contains light-absorbing molecules

_______________ **2.** A series of chemical reactions that produces sugars from carbon dioxide

_______________ **3.** A series of proteins in the thylakoid membrane that transfers high-energy electrons

_______________ **4.** Two groups of molecules in the thylakoid membrane that capture and transfer energy

_______________ **5.** Reaction that captures energy from sunlight and transfers energy to the light-independent reactions

_______________ **6.** Light-absorbing molecule in thylakoid membrane

Name Period Date

B. Stepped-Out Vocabulary Define each word. Then write two additional facts that are related to the word.

WORD	DEFINITION	MORE INFORMATION
Example ATP	*molecule that transfers energy from breakdown of food molecules to cell processes*	*three phosphate groups*
		forms cycle with ADP
1. aerobic		
2. glycolysis		
3. ADP		
4. fermentation		
5. cellular respiration		
6. anaerobic		
7. Krebs cycle		
8. lactic acid		

C. Word Origins Circle the Greek and Latin word parts in each vocabulary term. Then use the Greek and Latin meanings to construct a very basic definition of the vocabulary word.

tri-	=	three	photo-	=	light	an-	=	without
di-	=	two	syn-	=	together	-ic	=	relating to
chemo-	=	chemical	aero-	=	air	-ase	=	enzyme

WORD	DEFINITION
1. aerobic	
2. anaerobic	
3. photosystem	
4. chemosynthesis	
5. photosynthesis	
6. ATP synthase	

D. Analogy Vocabulary Set The vocabulary terms below are related to energy and the transfer of energy. On one blank line next to each vocabulary term, write the letter and number of the definition that best matches. On the other blank line, write the letter and number of the analogy that best matches.

DEFINITIONS	WORD	ANALOGIES
D1. the process that splits glucose into 2 three-carbon molecules and makes 2 ATP	**1.** ADP _____ _____	**A1.** an empty gas tank
D2. a low-energy molecule	**2.** electron transport chain _____ _____	**A2.** chopping a log in half to get firewood to burn
D3. a complex enzyme that makes ATP	**3.** glycolysis _____ _____	**A3.** a full gas tank
D4. a high-energy molecule that transfers energy to cell processes	**4.** ATP _____ _____	**A4.** a turbine that produces electricity from the flow of water
D5. series of proteins that transfers high-energy electrons	**5.** ATP synthase _____ _____	**A5.** a pipe that carries water to a turbine to produce electricity

E. Do-It Yourself Matching In a random order, write short definitions for each term on the blank lines to the right. Then give your paper to a classmate who should write the number of the term next to the correct definition.

1. thylakoid ____ ______________________

2. fermentation ____ ______________________

3. light-independent reactions ____ ______________________

4. anaerobic ____ ______________________

5. lactic acid ____ ______________________

6. chemosynthesis ____ ______________________

F. Vector Vocabulary Define the words in the boxes. On the line across each arrow, write a phrase that describes how the words in the boxes are related to each other.

GLYCOLYSIS
1. ______________________

2. ______________________

8. ______________________

CELLULAR RESPIRATION
3. ______________________

4. ______________________

KREBS CYCLE
5. ______________________

6. ______________________

ELECTRON TRANSPORT CHAIN
7. ______________________

FERMENTATION
9. ______________________

10. ______________________

LACTIC ACID
11. ______________________

Name Period Date

SECTION **5.1** THE CELL CYCLE
Study Guide

KEY CONCEPT
Cells have distinct phases of growth, reproduction, and normal functions.

VOCABULARY	
cell cycle	cytokinesis
mitosis	

MAIN IDEA: **The cell cycle has four main stages.**
Summarize what happens during each stage of the cell cycle in the boxes below.

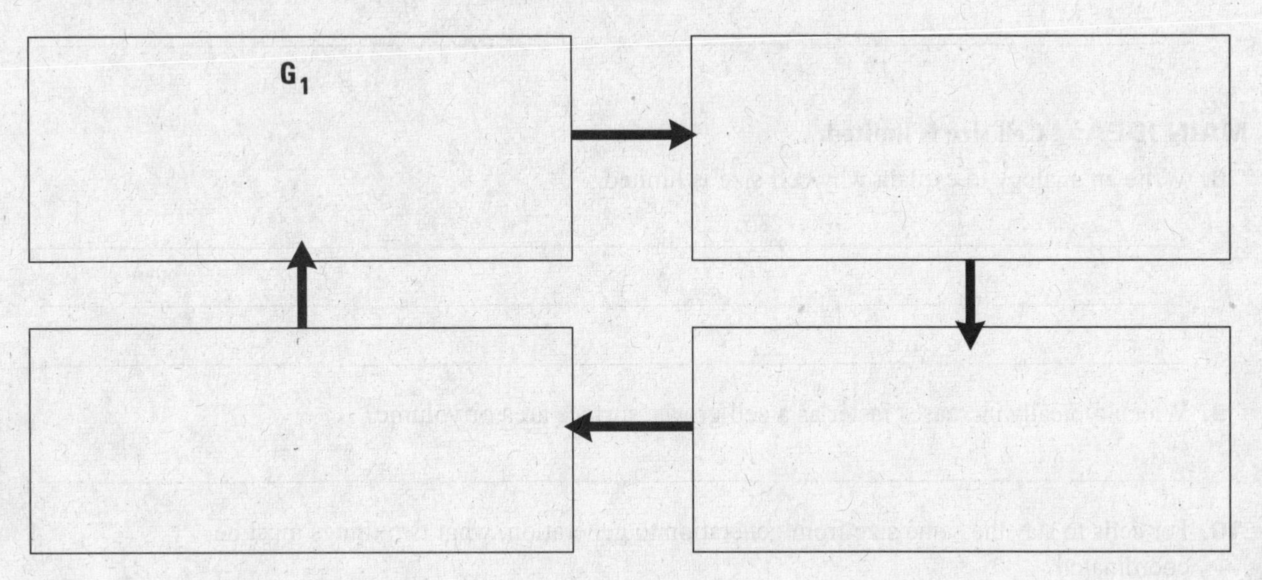

1. How did the G_1 and G_2 stages get their names?

2. Cells must pass through a critical checkpoint during which two stages of the cell cycle?

3. Where does DNA synthesis happen in eukaryotic cells?

4. What two processes make up the M stage?

MAIN IDEA: Cells divide at different rates.

5. Among different types of cells, which stage of the cell cycle varies most in length?

6. Why does a skin cell divide more often than a liver cell?

7. What is G_0?

MAIN IDEA: Cell size is limited.

8. Write an analogy to explain why cell size is limited.

9. Which typically increases faster as a cell grows, surface area or volume?

10. For cells to stay the same size from generation to generation, what two things must be coordinated?

Vocabulary Check

11. Think of an example of a cycle. What does this cycle have in common with the cell cycle?

12. What process divides a cell's cytoplasm? How do the two word parts of your answer help you remember it?

13. What process divides the cell nucleus and its contents?

Name Period Date

SECTION 5.1 | THE CELL CYCLE
Power Notes

Cell Cycle
Label each step and list the major events of each step where indicated.

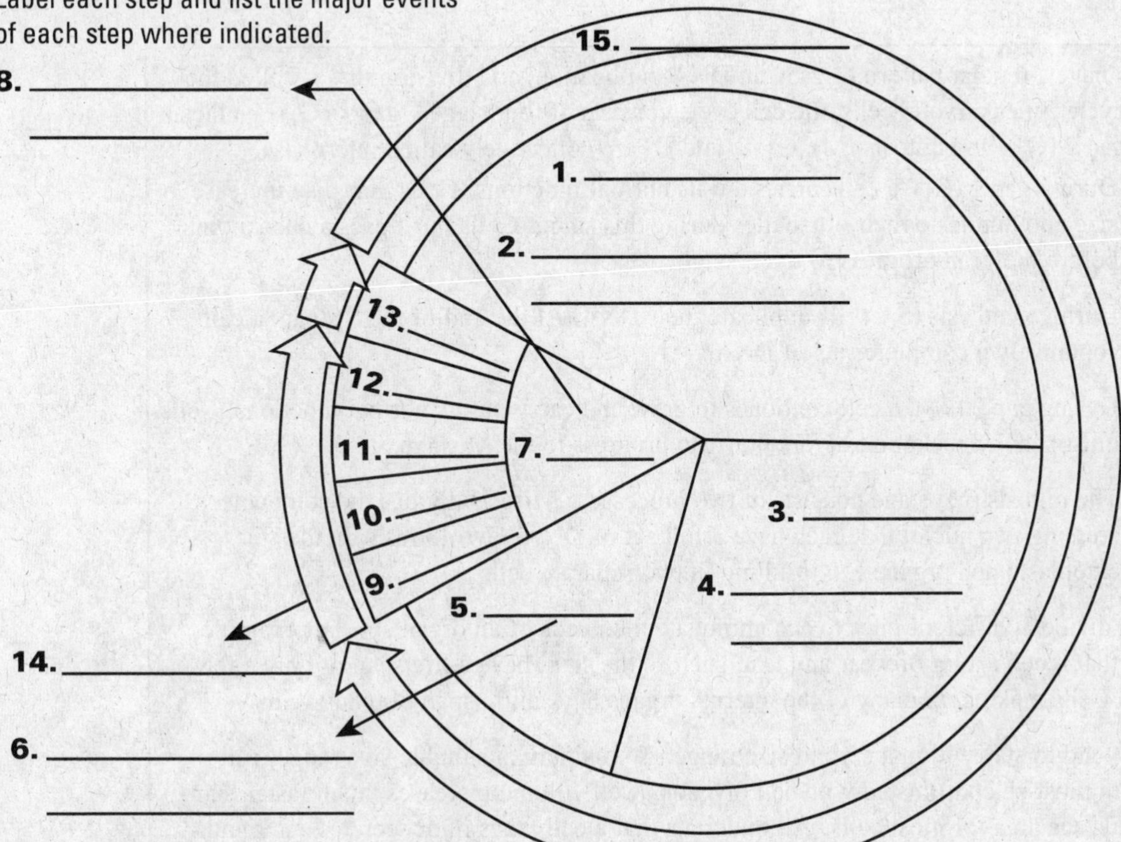

Cells divide at different rates.

Cell size is limited.
-
-
-

Circle the cube with the greatest surface area-to-volume ratio.

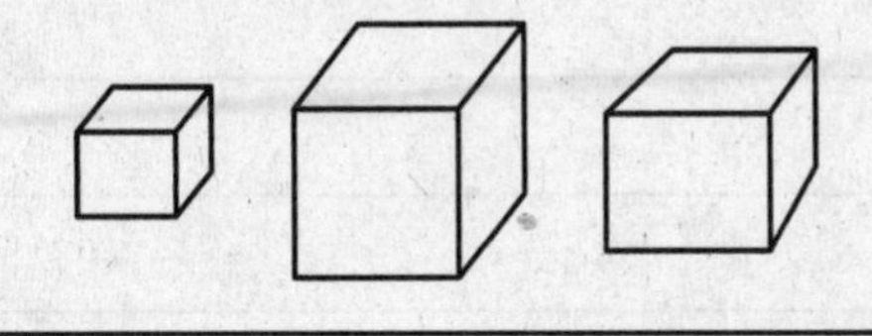

CHAPTER 5
Cell Growth and Division

Name Period Date

SECTION 5.1 | THE CELL CYCLE

Reinforcement

KEY CONCEPT Cells have distinct phases of growth, reproduction, and normal functions.

Cells have a regular pattern of growth, DNA duplication, and division that is called the **cell cycle.** In eukaryotic cells, the cell cycle consists of four stages: gap 1 (G_1), synthesis (S), gap 2 (G_2), and mitosis (M). G_1, S, and G_2 are collectively called interphase.

- During gap 1 (G_1), a cell carries out its normal functions. Cells may also increase in size and duplicate their organelles during this stage. Cells must pass a checkpoint before they can progress to the S stage.
- During synthesis (S), cells duplicate their DNA. At the end of the S stage, a cell contains two complete sets of DNA.
- During gap 2 (G_2), a cell continues to grow and carry out its normal functions. Cells must pass a checkpoint before they can progress to the M stage.
- The mitosis (M) stage consists of two processes. **Mitosis** divides the cell nucleus, creating two nuclei that each have a full set of DNA. **Cytokinesis** divides the cytoplasm and organelles, resulting in two separate cells.

Cells divide at different rates to accommodate the needs of an organism. For example, cells that receive a lot of wear and tear, such as the skin, have a life span of only a few days. Cells making up many of the internal organs have a life span of many years.

Cells tend to stay within a certain size range. To maintain a suitable size range, cell growth must be coordinated with cell division. Cell volume increases much faster than cell surface area for most cells. All materials that a cell takes in or secretes enter and exit through the membrane. The cell's surface area must be large enough relative to its overall volume in order for the cell to get its necessary materials. Therefore, most cells tend to be very small.

1. What are the four stages of the cell cycle?

____

2. What two processes make up the M phase of the cell cycle?

____

3. Why don't cells all divide at the same rate?

____

____

____

Name Period Date

SECTION **5.2** | MITOSIS AND CYTOKINESIS

Study Guide

KEY CONCEPT
Cells divide during mitosis and cytokinesis.

VOCABULARY		
chromosome	centromere	metaphase
histone	telomere	anaphase
chromatin	prophase	telophase
chromatid		

MAIN IDEA: Chromosomes condense at the start of mitosis.

1. What is a chromosome?

____

2. Why do chromosomes condense at the start of mitosis?

____

3. Why are chromosomes not condensed during all stages of the cell cycle?

____

____

Refer to Figure 5.5 to sketch how DNA goes from a long stringy form to a tightly condensed form. Label the parts of the condensed, duplicated chromosome.

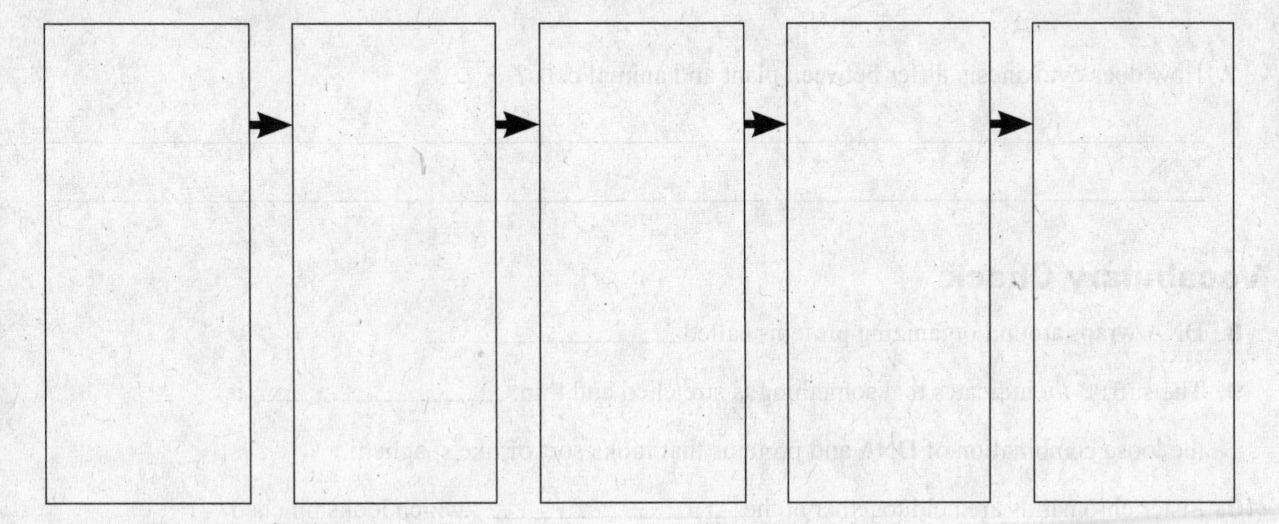

MAIN IDEA: Mitosis and cytokinesis produce two genetically identical daughter cells.

4. How does interphase prepare a cell to divide?

____

5. Mitosis occurs in what types of cells?

____

6. Develop a device, such as a short sentence or phrase, to help you remember the order of the steps of mitosis: prophase, metaphase, anaphase, telophase.

____

Complete the diagram illustrating the four phases of mitosis and one phase of cytokinesis.

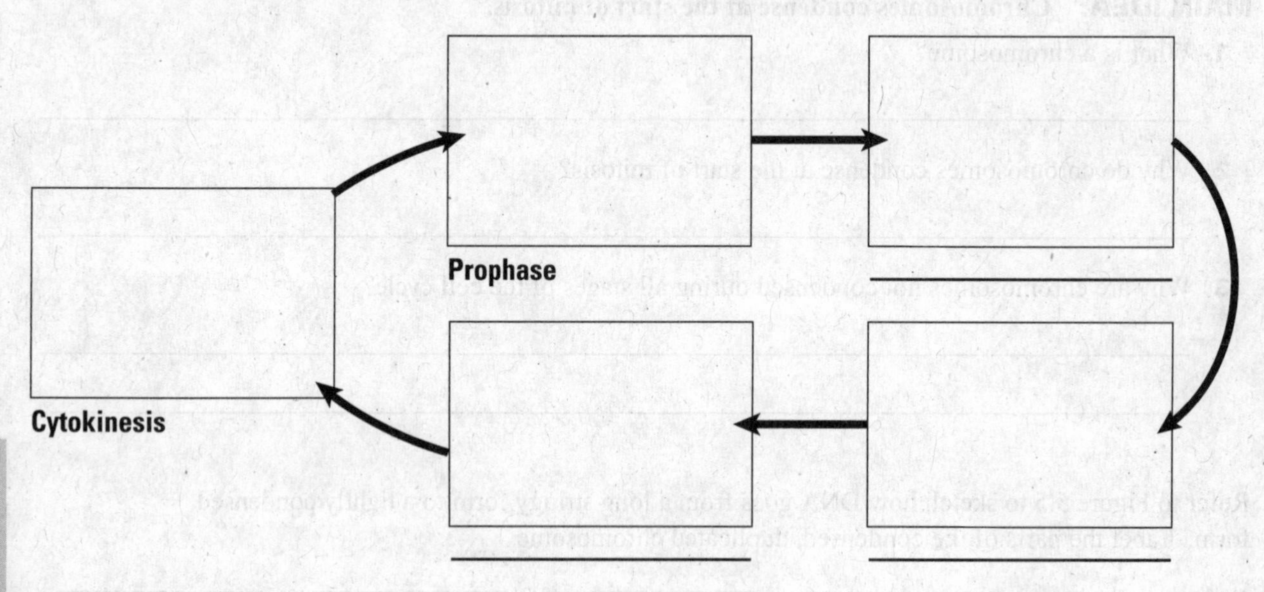

7. How does cytokinesis differ between plant and animal cells?

____

____

Vocabulary Check

8. DNA wraps around organizing proteins called ______________.

9. The suffix *-tin* indicates that something is stretched and thin. ______________ is the loose combination of DNA and proteins that looks sort of like spaghetti.

10. Sister chromatids are held together at the ______________, which looks pinched.

11. The ends of DNA molecules form structures called ______________ that help prevent the loss of genes.

Name Period Date

SECTION 5.2 | MITOSIS AND CYTOKINESIS

Power Notes

Chromosome structure:

-
-
-
-

Cell Cycle in Detail

Identify the steps below and list the major events of each step.

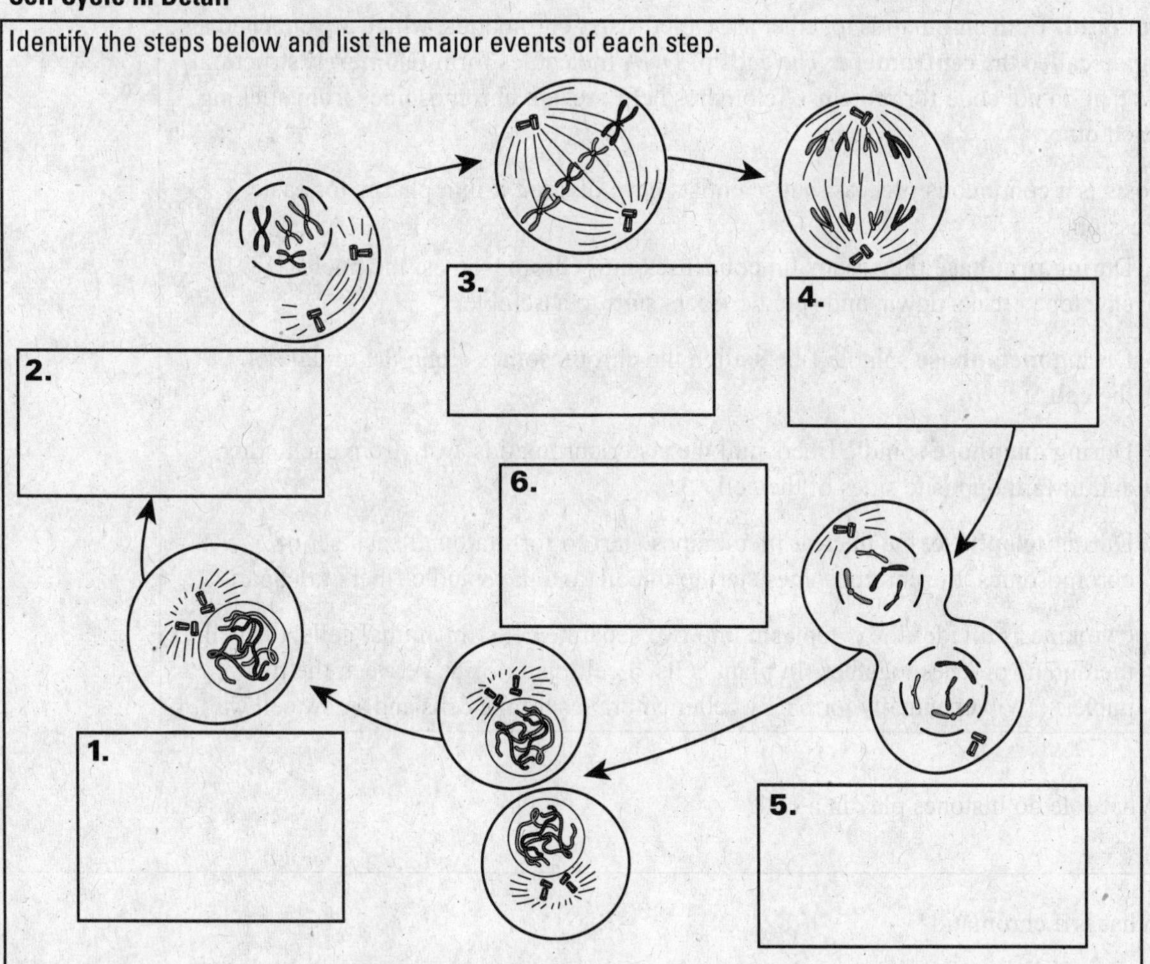

Name Period Date

SECTION **5.2** MITOSIS AND CYTOKINESIS

Reinforcement

KEY CONCEPT Cells divide during mitosis and cytokinesis.

During interphase, a cell needs access to its DNA to make use of specific genes and to copy the DNA. During mitosis, however, the DNA must be condensed and organized so that it can be accurately divided between the two nuclei. DNA is a long polymer made of repeating subunits called nucleotides. Each long continuous thread of DNA is called a **chromosome,** and each chromosome has many genes.

During interphase, DNA wraps around organizing proteins called **histones** and is loosely organized as **chromatin,** which looks sort of like spaghetti. As a cell prepares for mitosis, however, the DNA and histones start to coil more and more tightly until they form condensed chromosomes. Each half of the duplicated chromosome is called a **chromatid.** Both chromatids together are called sister chromatids, which are attached at a region called the **centromere.** The ends of DNA molecules form **telomeres,** structural units that do not code for proteins. Telomeres help prevent chromosomes from sticking to each other.

Mitosis is a continuous process, but scientists have divided it into phases for easier discussion.

- During **prophase** the chromatin condenses into chromosomes, the nuclear envelope breaks down, and spindle fibers start to assemble.
- During **metaphase** spindle fibers align the chromosomes along the middle of the cell.
- During **anaphase** spindle fibers pull the sister chromatids away from each other and toward opposite sides of the cell.
- During **telophase,** the nuclear membranes start to form around each set of chromosomes, the chromosomes start to uncoil, and the spindle fibers fall apart.
- Cytokinesis divides the cytoplasm into two separate cells. In animal cells, the cell membrane pinches together. In plant cells, a cell plate forms between the two nuclei. It will eventually form new cell membranes for the cells and a new cell wall.

1. What role do histones play in a cell?

____

2. What is a chromatid?

____

3. During which phase of mitosis are sister chromatids separated from each other?

____

Name Period Date

SECTION **5.3** | REGULATION OF THE CELL CYCLE

Study Guide

KEY CONCEPT
Cell cycle regulation is necessary for healthy growth.

VOCABULARY		
growth factor	benign	carcinogen
apoptosis	malignant	
cancer	metastasize	

MAIN IDEA: Internal and external factors regulate cell division.
Complete the concept map below to show important ideas about growth factors.

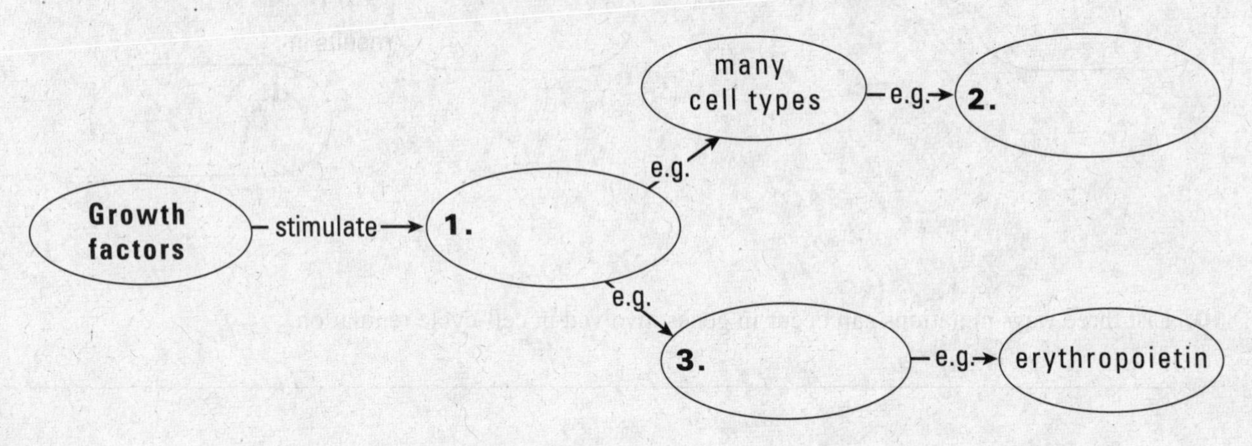

Use the word bank to complete the sequence diagram below.

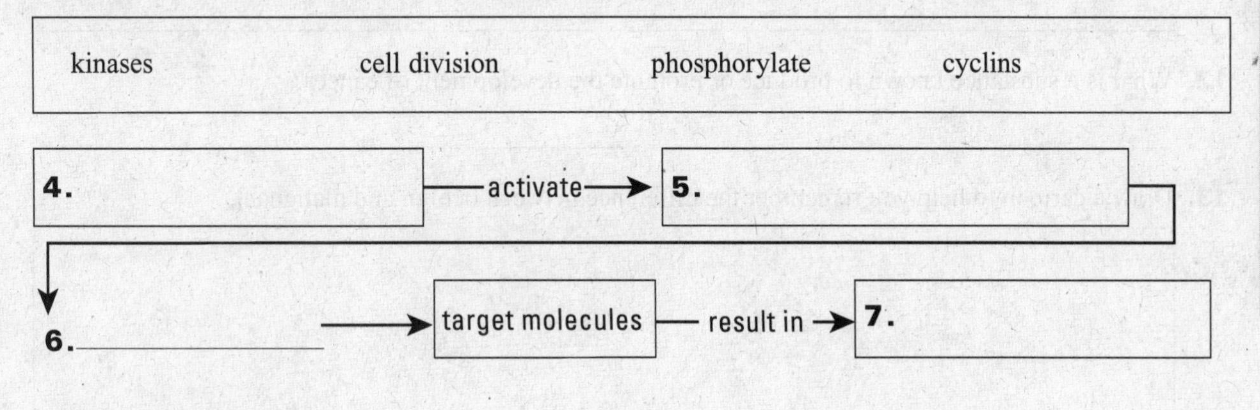

8. What is apoptosis?

____

MAIN IDEA: Cell division is uncontrolled in cancer.

9. What type of disease may result if cell division is not properly regulated?

____

Name Period Date

Complete the concept map below about cancer cells.

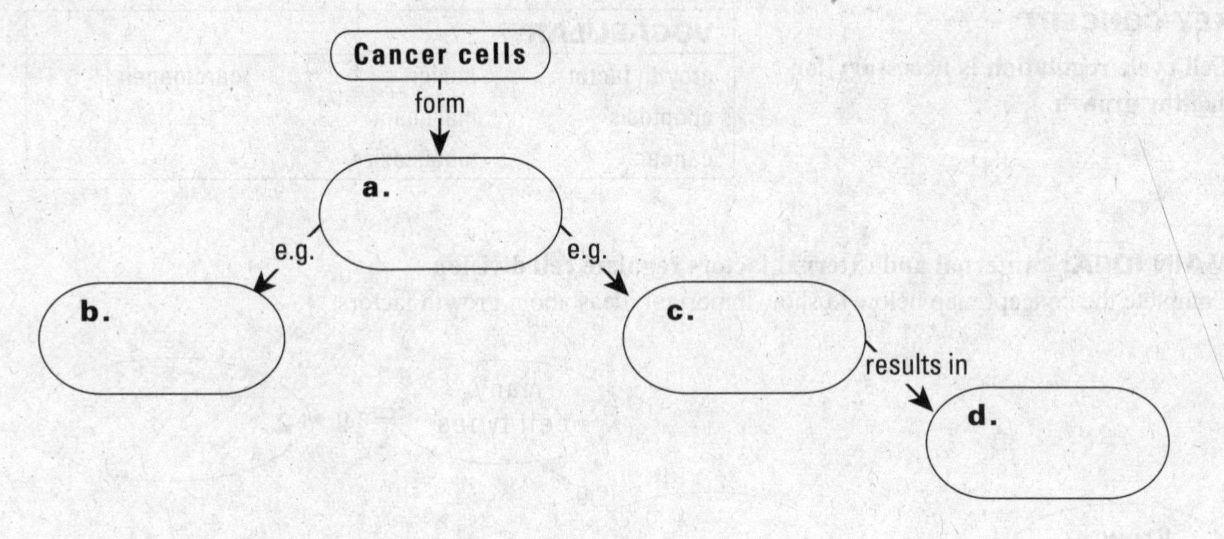

10. List three ways mutations can occur in genes involved in cell-cycle regulation.

Vocabulary Check

11. What does metastasize mean?

12. What is a substance known to produce or promote the development of cancer?

13. Draw a cartoon to help you remember the difference between benign and malignant.

Name Period Date

SECTION 5.3 | REGULATION OF THE CELL CYCLE

Power Notes

Internal factors:

External factors:

Cell Cycle

Carcinogens:

• Examples:

Cancer cells

may form

may be killed by

Tumors

Apoptosis

Malignant

Benign

Examples of apoptosis in healthy organisms:

•

•

Name Period Date

SECTION 5.3 REGULATION OF THE CELL CYCLE

Reinforcement

KEY CONCEPT Cell cycle regulation is necessary for healthy growth.

The cell cycle is regulated by both external and internal factors. External factors come from outside the cell. These include cell–cell contact, which prevents further growth of normal cells, and chemical signals called growth factors. **Growth factors** stimulate cells to divide. Most cells respond to a combination of growth factors, not just one. Some growth factors affect many different types of cells. Others specifically affect one cell type. Internal factors come from inside the cell. Very often, an external factor triggers the activation of an internal factor. A cyclin is a type of internal factor. It activates kinases, which in turn, add a phosphate group to other molecules that help drive the cell cycle forward.

Cells not only regulate growth, but also death. **Apoptosis** is programmed cell death. Apoptosis plays important roles in development and metamorphosis.

When a cell loses control over its cycle of growth and division, **cancer** may result. Cancer cells can continue to divide despite cell–cell contact or a lack of growth factors. Cancer cells form disorganized clumps of cells called tumors. **Benign** tumors tend to remain clumped together and may be cured by removal. **Malignant** tumors have cells that break away, or **metastasize,** and spread to other parts of the body, forming new tumors. Malignant tumors are more difficult to treat than benign tumors. Radiation therapy and chemotherapy are common treatments for cancer. However, both treatments kill healthy cells as well as cancer cells.

Cancer cells can arise from normal cells that have experienced damage to their genes involved in cell cycle regulation. Damage may arise from inherited errors in genes, from mutations carried by viruses, and from carcinogens. **Carcinogens** are substances known to produce or promote the development of cancer. These include substances such as tobacco smoke and other air pollutants.

1. List two examples of external factors that influence the cell cycle.

____

2. What is apoptosis?

____

3. How does a benign tumor differ from a malignant tumor?

____

____

____

Name Period Date

SECTION 5.4 | ASEXUAL REPRODUCTION

Study Guide

KEY CONCEPT

Many organisms reproduce by cell division.

VOCABULARY
asexual reproduction
binary fission

MAIN IDEA: Binary fission is similar in function to mitosis.

1. Offspring resulting from asexual reproduction and those resulting from sexual reproduction differ in one major way. What is the difference?

____

Sketch the steps of binary fission in the boxes below. Beside each sketch, write a brief description of what is occurring.

2. ______________________________

3. ______________________________

4. ______________________________

Name Period Date

STUDY GUIDE, CONTINUED

Fill in the chart below to highlight the advantages and disadvantages of asexual reproduction.

Advantages	Disadvantages
5.	
6.	
7.	

MAIN IDEA: Some eukaryotes reproduce through mitosis.

8. If a eukaryotic organism reproduces through mitosis, what is true about the offspring and the parent organism?

9. In what types of organisms is mitotic reproduction most common?

10. List three examples of mitotic reproduction.

11. What forms of reproduction does the sea anemone use?

Vocabulary Check

12. Write a word that starts with the letters "bi." Explain what is similar between the meaning of the word you wrote and the meaning of "binary fission."

13. What is the creation of offspring from only one parent organism called?

Name Period Date

SECTION **5.4** | ASEXUAL REPRODUCTION
Power Notes

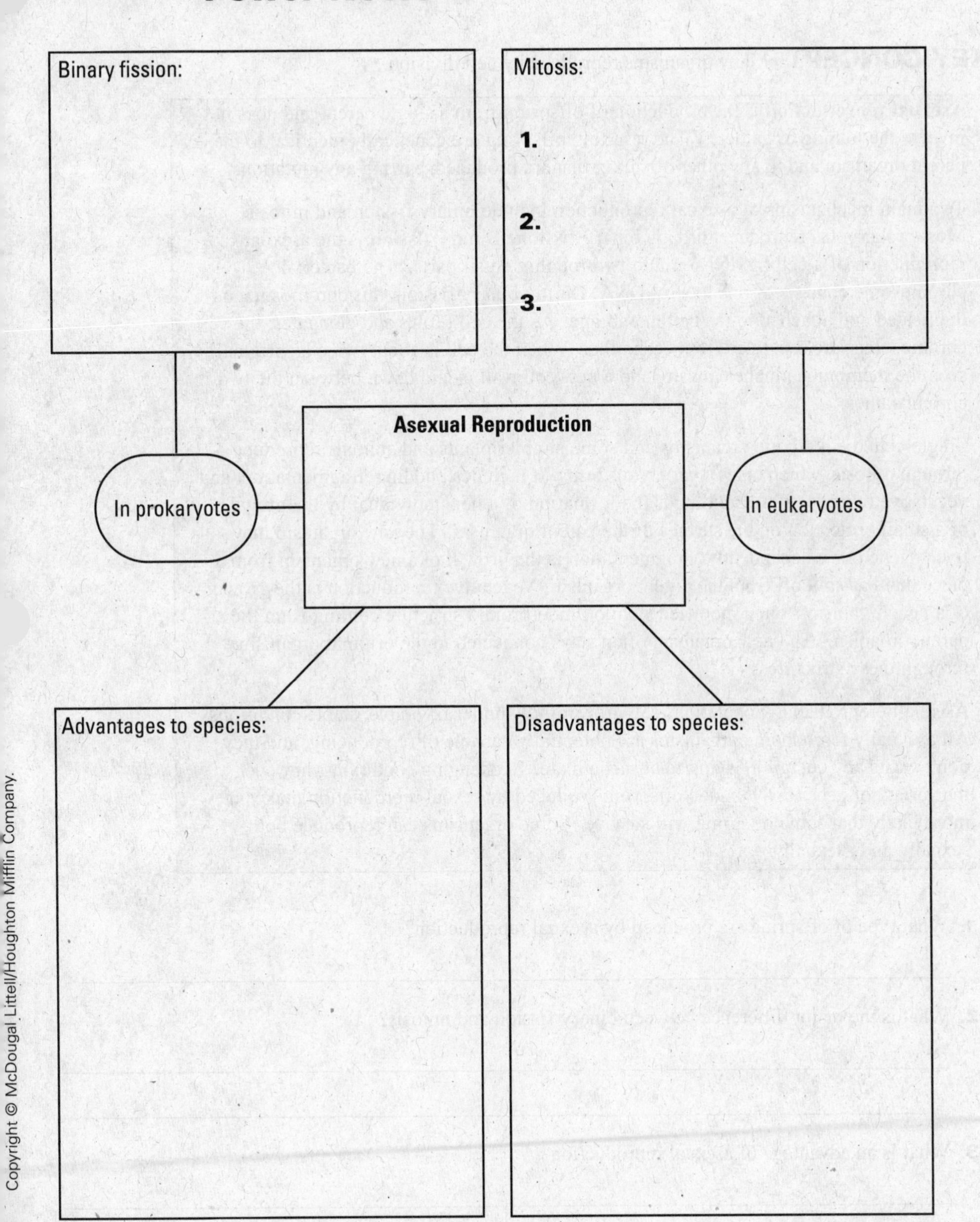

CHAPTER 5
Cell Growth and Division

Name Period Date

SECTION **5.4** ASEXUAL REPRODUCTION

Reinforcement

KEY CONCEPT Many organisms reproduce by cell division.

Asexual reproduction is the production of offspring from a single parent and does not involve the joining of gametes. The resulting offspring are genetically identical to the parent organism and to any other offspring that are produced, barring any mutations.

Two main mechanisms of asexual reproduction include binary fission and mitosis. Most prokaryotes reproduce through binary fission. **Binary fission** is the asexual reproduction of a cell by division into two roughly equal parts. The bacterial chromosome consists of one loop of DNA. During binary fission, this chromosome is duplicated and attached to the cell membrane. As the cell grows and elongates, the chromosomes are separated from each other. When the cell is about twice its original size, the membrane pinches inward, and a new cell wall is laid down between the two chromosomes.

Single-celled eukaryotic organisms and some simpler plants and animals reproduce through mitosis, which takes a variety of forms. It includes budding, fragmentation, and vegetative reproduction. Budding is the formation of a new individual by the growth of a small projection on the surface of the parent organism. The new organism may live attached or independently. Fragmentation is the growth of a new organism from a piece that has split off from the parent organism. Vegetative reproduction is the growth of a new organism from a modified stem or underground structure coming from the parent organism. The new organism often stays connected to the original organism through these structures.

Asexually reproducing populations can grow rapidly under favorable, stable conditions. All asexually reproducing organisms are potentially capable of reproducing, and they don't waste any energy in trying to attract a mate. In changing conditions, however, the variety of genetically unique offspring produced by sexual reproduction makes it more likely that some offspring will survive. Some organisms can reproduce both sexually and asexually.

1. What type of offspring are produced by asexual reproduction?

____

2. What is the major difference between binary fission and mitosis?

____

____

3. What is an advantage of asexual reproduction?

____

____

Name Period Date

SECTION **5.5** MULTICELLULAR LIFE

Study Guide

KEY CONCEPT

Cells work together to carry out complex functions.

VOCABULARY		
tissue	organ system	stem cell
organ	cell differentiation	

MAIN IDEA: Multicellular organisms depend on interactions among different cell types.

Complete the diagram below that represents organization in multicellular organisms.

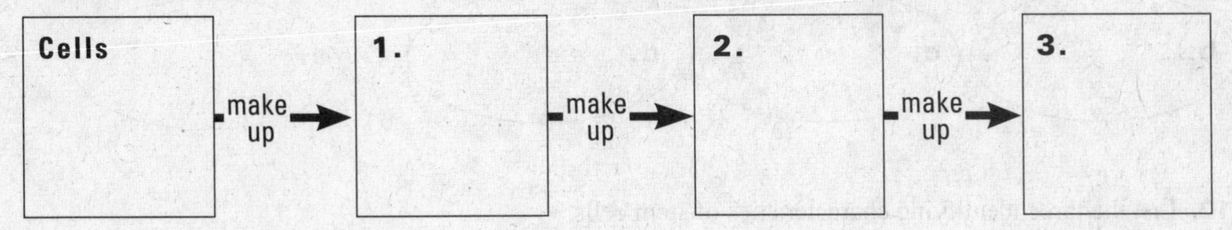

4. List two examples of tissues found in plants.

____

5. List two examples of organ systems found in plants.

____

6. How does an organism benefit from organ systems that work together and communicate?

____

MAIN IDEA: Specialized cells perform specific functions.

7. What is the process by which unspecialized cells develop into specialized cells?

____

8. Do different types of cells have different DNA? Explain.

____

9. What role does cell location play within a developing embryo?

____

MAIN IDEA: Stem cells can develop into different cell types.

Complete the concept map below about stem cell classification.

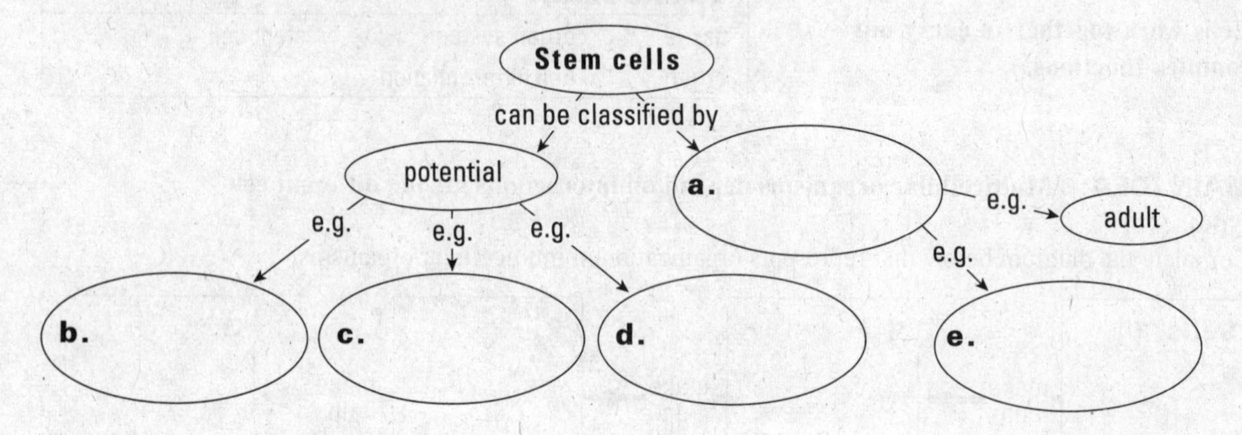

10. List the three identifying characteristics of stem cells.

____

____

____

11. List one advantage of using adult stem cells and one advantage of using embryonic stem cells.

____

____

Vocabulary Check

12. What is cell differentiation?

____

13. Write the following words in order from the largest structure to the smallest structure: cell, organ, organ system, tissue

____

Name Period Date

SECTION **5.5** MULTICELLULAR LIFE

Power Notes

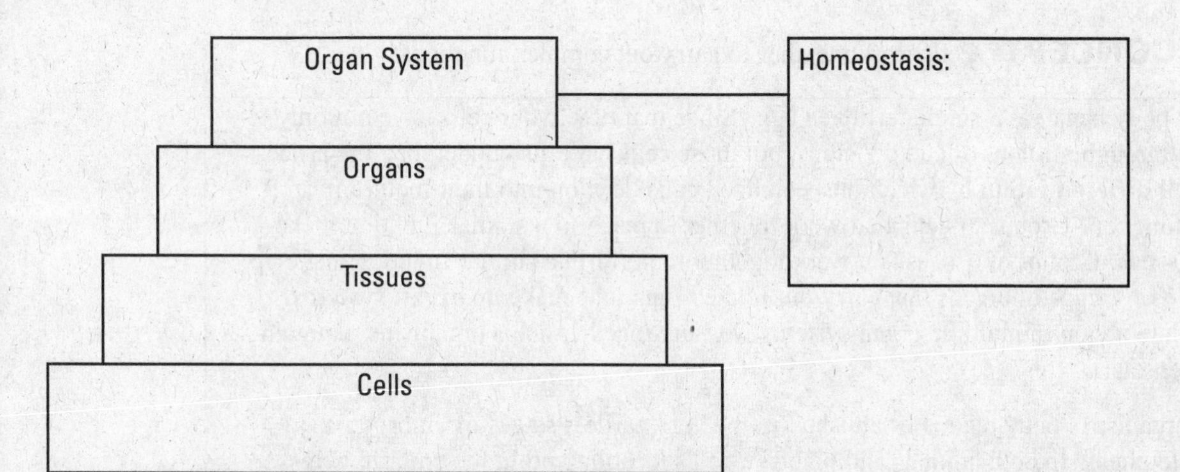

Defining characteristics:

1.

2.

3.

Potential:

1.

2.

3.

Stem Cells

Possible uses:

Origin:

1.

2.

CHAPTER 5
Cell Growth and Division

Name Period Date

SECTION **5.5** MULTICELLULAR LIFE

Reinforcement

KEY CONCEPT Cells work together to carry out complex functions.

Your body began as a single fertilized egg. Since that time, your cells have not only gone through millions of cell divisions, but those cells have also undergone the process of **cell differentiation** by which unspecialized cells develop into their mature form and function. Groups of cells that work together to perform a similar function make up **tissues.** Groups of tissues that work together to perform a similar function make up **organs.** Groups of organs that carry out related functions make up **organ systems.** The interaction of multiple organ systems working together helps organisms maintain homeostasis.

An organism's body plan is established in the very earliest stages of embryonic development. In both animals and plants, a cell's location within the embryo helps determine how that cell will differentiate. In animals, cells migrate to specific areas that will determine how they specialize. Plant cells cannot readily migrate because of their cell walls. However, the cells remain very adaptable throughout the life of the plant.

Stem cells are a unique type of body cell characterized by three features:

- They divide and renew themselves for long periods of time.
- They remain undifferentiated in form.
- They can develop into a variety of specialized cell types.

Because of their ability to develop into other types of cells, stem cells offer great hope for curing damaged organs and currently untreatable diseases. However, they also raise many ethical concerns. Stem cells can be categorized by their developmental potential, as totipotent, pluripotent, or multipotent. Stem cells can also be classified by origin, as adult or embryonic.

1. What is cell differentiation?

____

____

2. What are three distinguishing characteristics of stem cells?

____

____

____

Name Period Date

CHAPTER 5

CONSTRUCTING DATA TABLES

Data Analysis Practice

Colchicine is a drug used to help treat patients with gout, a condition in which people have too much uric acid build up in their blood and joints. Although colchicine can be used successfully to reduce inflammation, some patients experience side effects, including diarrhea, vomiting, hives, ulcers in the mouth, and blood in the urine.

Suppose you are asked to organize the results of a hypothetical experiment that calculated the percentage of patients who experienced side effects from taking colchicine at different dosages. The information from the experiment is as follows: at 0.5 mg dosage, 2% of patients had side effects; at 1.0 mg dosage, 5% of patients reported side effects; at 1.5 mg dosage, 7% of patients experience side effects; at 2.0 mg dosage, 10% of patients had side effects; at 2.5 mg dosage, 11.5% of patients had side effects; at 3.0 mg dosage, 13% of patients felt side effects; at 3.5 mg dosage, 15% of patients had side effects; at 4.0 mg dosage, 17.5% of patients reported side effects; at 4.5 mg dosage, 20% of patients experienced side effects; at 5.0 mg dosage, 23% of patients had side effects; at 5.5 mg dosage, 27.5% of patients had side effects; at 6.0 mg dosage, 32% of patients felt side effects.

1. **Organize Data** Construct and complete a data table that organizes the data.

2. **Analyze** According to the data, what is the relationship between dosage amounts and side effects felt by patients?

____

____

CHAPTER 5 Cell Growth and Division

CHAPTER 5 | SPINDLES AND MITOSIS

Pre-AP Activity

In Chapter 5, you have learned about the stages of mitosis. For mitosis to occur, sister chromatids must move to opposite poles. This allows the DNA to be equally distributed and two genetically identical daughter cells to be produced. In this activity, you will learn how spindle fibers grow and shrink.

PROPHASE

At prophase, each chromosome consists of two sister chromatids held together at the centromere. Two disk-shaped regions, called kinetochores, are located on opposite sides of the centromere, with each kinetochore attached to a chromatid.

In the cytoplasm, the spindle apparatus begins to form. Spindle fibers are made up of microtubules, hollow cylinders composed of the protein tubulin. It is likely that the spindle is assembled from microtubule components of the cell's cytoskeleton. Formation of the spindle takes place in the two centrosomes, organelles that organize microtubules. The centrosomes, with bundles of forming spindle fibers trailing behind them, move to opposite poles of the cell, called the spindle poles. One end of the fiber in a spindle fiber bundle becomes attached to a chromosome at the chromosome's kinetochore. Remember that the other end of the fiber bundle is attached to a spindle pole. The number of microtubules in a bundle attaching to each kinetochore varies in different species; there may be only one or two or more than 100 microtubules on each kinetochore.

METAPHASE

When the spindle apparatus has completely formed, the two chromatids of each chromosome are attached to opposite spindle poles by microtubules. During metaphase, the chromosomes begin to move in jerky motions as the spindle fibers pull them into position at the cell's equator. You can think of this movement as a tug-of-war with each chromosome being pulled in two directions by the spindle poles.

ANAPHASE

Anaphase begins suddenly when the centromere splits. The separated chromatids, now called chromosomes, are dragged to opposite poles of the cell by the spindle fibers attached to the kinetochores.

THE ROLE OF SPINDLE FIBERS

The microtubules that make up spindle fibers alternate between growing (polymerization) during prophase and shrinking (depolymerization) during anaphase. This process, called dynamic instability, is achieved by either adding or losing tubulin subunits made of α–tubulin (alpha tubulin) and β–tubulin (beta tubulin) proteins. The polarity of the subunits produces regular, parallel orientation along the microtubule. The α–tubulin end is the negative end and the β–tubulin end is the positive end. The growing and shrinking of the microtubules is thought to be controlled by GTP, guanosine triphosphate.

- Growing free tubulin subunits contain a tightly bound GTP molecule that is hydrolyzed into GDP (guanosine diphosphate) when the subunit attaches to the free end (positive end) of the microtubule. If polymerization occurs quickly, the GTP in the newly added tubulin subunit may not be able to be hydrolyzed as quickly and build up. This results in the positive end of the microtubule being composed of only GTP-containing tubulin subunits. These subunits bind tightly together forming a GTP cap which prevents depolymerization.

- Shrinking is possible when the tubulin subunit at the free end of the microtubule hydrolyzes the GTP before the next tubulin subunit is added. If this happens, then the tubulin subunits at the end of the microtubule will be composed of only GDP. Since GDP-containing tubulin molecules are less tightly bound and are more easily released, the microtubule will shrink.

Answer the following questions on a separate piece of paper.

1. In what stages of mitosis would you expect to find mostly polymerization taking place? mostly depolymerization? Explain your answers.
2. The drug colchicine binds tightly to free tubulin subunits and prevents polymerization. The drug taxol binds tightly to microtubules and prevents them from losing tubulin subunits but allows new molecules to attach. Explain how these drugs would affect spindle fibers and the process of mitosis.
3. How could the use of colchicine and taxol be beneficial in the treatment of cancer?
4. Using the diagram of a microtubule below, illustrate how polymerization changes the size of the microtubule. Include in your illustration a GTP cap that stops growth (see key).

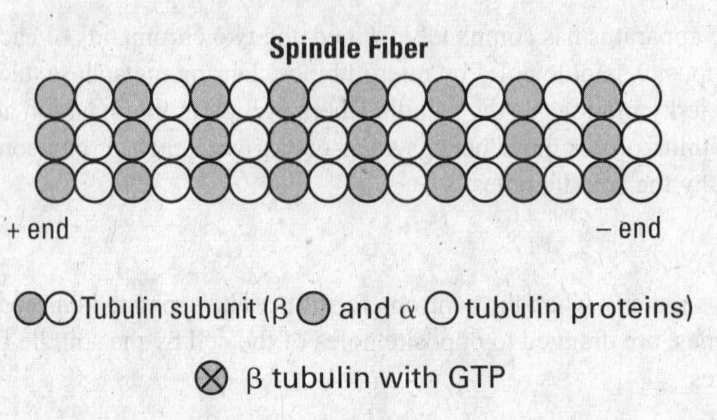

Name Period Date

CHAPTER 5

HeLa CELLS

Pre-AP Activity

In Chapter 5, you have learned that cancer is a disease that results from a breakdown in the regulation of the cell cycle. A great deal of scientific research has been—and is being—carried out on cancer cells so scientists can learn more about these diseases. Where did these cancer cells come from?

STANDARD CELL LINES

To avoid introducing an additional variable in their experiments and to make their experiments repeatable, researchers use standard cell lines—cells that have been cultured in the lab and are available to the scientific community. Most cells live for a short time outside the body, then age and die. A few cell lines are considered to be immortal because they continue to grow and divide indefinitely when provided with the correct culture conditions. HeLa cells are an example of an immortalized cell line. They have been grown under laboratory conditions for thousands of cell generations and are used extensively in medical research. HeLa cells are human epithelial cells from a fatal cervical tumor. Here is their story.

HeLa CELLS

In 1951, Henrietta Lacks, a 31-year-old, African-American mother of five children, died of cervical cancer in Baltimore. Before she died, doctors removed some of the cells from her tumor and delivered them to Dr. George Gey, head of tissue culture research at the Johns Hopkins University. Dr. Gey was looking for cells that would continue to grow and divide in the lab. He grew the tumor cells in his test tubes and was amazed at how fast they divided and how strong they were. Within a few months of Henrietta's death, her cells were still alive, and Dr. Gey was using them to grow polio viruses. But neither Henrietta nor her family knew that her cells had been taken and that they lived on.

Gey named the cells *HeLa* after the first two letters of Henrietta's first and last names. HeLa cells were—and still are—among the strongest cells known to science. Especially valuable was their ability to divide every 24 hours. Dr. Gey sent them to researchers around the world. Demand grew, and the cells were soon mass-produced. And still Henrietta's family did not know of their existence. The cells were used in cancer and AIDS research, in creating a polio vaccine, in gene mapping, in testing the effects of radiation and drugs, and in many other types of medical research. HeLa cells were even sent to space on the space shuttle at one point.

By the early 1970s, some researchers began to suspect that HeLa cells had contaminated their other cell lines. They couldn't be sure because they had little information about the identity of HeLa cells. DNA testing was unknown in the 1950s, when the HeLa line originated. At about the same time, Henrietta's children discovered by accident that their mother's cells still existed. They contacted the Johns Hopkins University and were asked to donate blood and tissue samples.

Researchers say the family was told that the tissue samples were needed so the HeLa cells could be genetically identified. Family members say they were told that the samples were needed to see if they were at risk of developing the same kind of cancer that killed Henrietta. They tried to get information from the researchers, but their questions went unanswered. To this day, the Lacks family has not received any compensation for the widespread use of Henrietta's cells.

Name Period Date

ETHICAL CONSIDERATIONS

Several ethical questions about the HeLa-cell story can be raised. Who owns Henrietta's cells? Do researchers need consent to take and use cells from a person? Does it matter that the cells are cancerous? Should Henrietta's family have been compensated for use of her cells? How do you place a monetary value on cells? Should this value vary according to their commercial value? Are cells worth more if they are used to develop a profitable vaccine?

BIOMEDICAL ETHICS

Today, people who work in the field of biomedical ethics try to answer or address the questions and concerns raised by situations such as Henrietta's. When patients go into a hospital for surgery, many will sign a form to indicate whether their tissues can be used for research, and they are promised that these samples will not be taken without their consent. However, many issues have not yet been resolved. Hospitals have thousands of blood and tissue samples already stored, and there are no rules governing who has access to these samples. Some bioethicists want laws passed that will require researchers to get permission before using tissue samples for research. Many researchers think that this requirement will slow or prevent scientific research.

The issue of who owns your cells and whether you can sell them also can be confusing. For example, you can sell your blood and your eggs or sperm, but you cannot sell your kidney. Does the human body have a price tag?

DEBATE

Consider the many ethical questions raised by the HeLa story. Conduct library or Internet research on these issues and the different points of view. Decide whether you think a person owns his or her cells or whether you think researchers should be able to use them freely. Consider whether a patient's identity should be protected or whether he or she should be identified.

Now, consider whether you would argue for or against some kind of monetary compensation for the use of Henrietta Lacks' cells, or what kind of legislation you think should be passed to deal with these matters. Imagine that you are a lawyer and you are making opening remarks to a judge or jury on this issue, or you are an advocate testifying before the government on what kind of laws should be written to resolve such issues. What are the main issues? What is at stake?

Name Period Date

CHAPTER 5 | CELL GROWTH AND DIVISION

Vocabulary Practice

cell cycle	prophase	metastasize
mitosis	metaphase	carcinogen
cytokinesis	anaphase	asexual reproduction
chromosome	telophase	binary fission
histone	growth factor	tissue
chromatin	apoptosis	organ
chromatid	cancer	organ system
centromere	benign	cell differentiation
telomere	malignant	stem cell

A. Analogy Vocabulary Set Write the numbers of the definitions and analogies next to each word.

DEFINITIONS	WORD	ANALOGIES
D1. makes offspring from one parent	**1.** benign ____ ____	**A1.** a twisty tie
D2. protein that DNA wraps around	**2.** chromatin ____ ____	**A2.** weeding
D3. loosely organized combination of DNA and proteins	**3.** asexual reproduction ____ ____	**A3.** fertilizer
D4. constricted region of DNA where sister chromatids are attached	**4.** organ system ____ ____	**A4.** making a copy
D5. tumor that remains in a clump	**5.** centromere ____ ____	**A5.** the cardboard tube inside a roll of toilet paper
D6. group of organs that work together to carry out a complex function	**6.** apoptosis ____ ____	**A6.** the United Nations
D7. programmed cell death	**7.** growth factor ____ ____	**A7.** a shy person who won't leave the house
D8. stimulates cell division	**8.** histone ____ ____	**A8.** tangled yarn

CHAPTER 5 Cell Growth and Division

Name Period Date

VOCABULARY PRACTICE, CONTINUED

B. Compound Word Puzzle Read the phrase and write the word that it most closely describes. Then write another phrase that describes the same word in a different way.

PHRASE 1	WORD	PHRASE 2
one half of a condensed, duplicated chromosome	**Example** chromatid	separates from sister chromatid during anaphase in mitosis
first phase of mitosis	**1.**	
may be categorized as totipotent, pluripotent, or multipotent	**2.**	
duplicated chromosomes line up along the cell equator	**3.**	
last phase of mitosis	**4.**	
spindle fibers pull the sister chromatids apart	**5.**	
a disease caused by a mutation in genes that control the cell cycle	**6.**	
divides a cell's cytoplasm	**7.**	
condenses at the start of mitosis	**8.**	

CHAPTER 5 Cell Growth and Division

C. Vector Vocabulary Define the words in the boxes. On the line across each arrow, write a phrase that describes how the words in the boxes are related to each other.

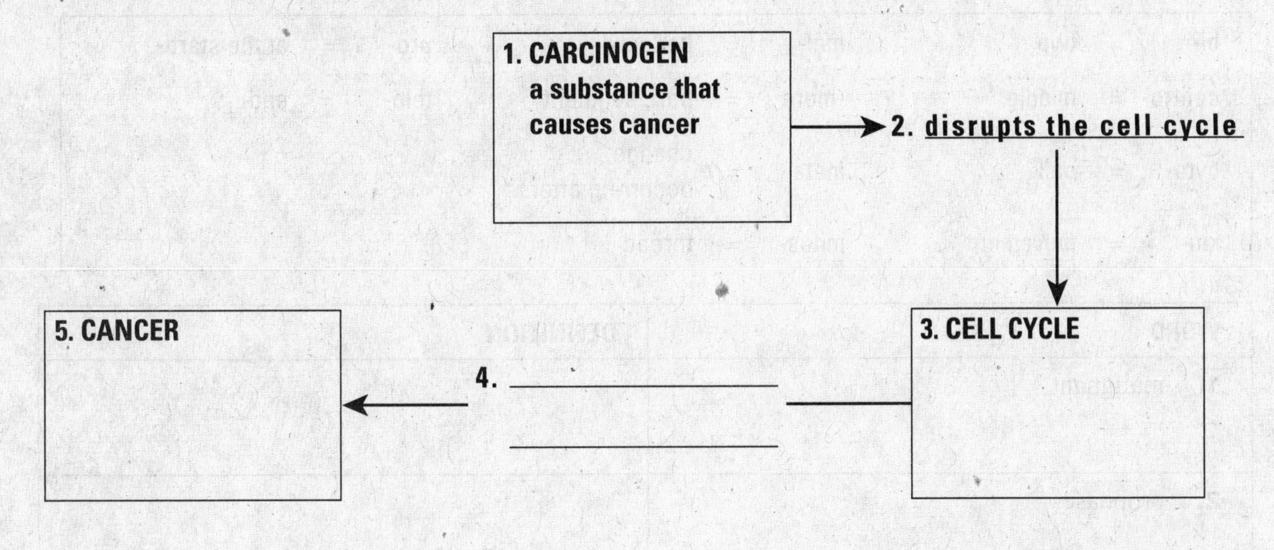

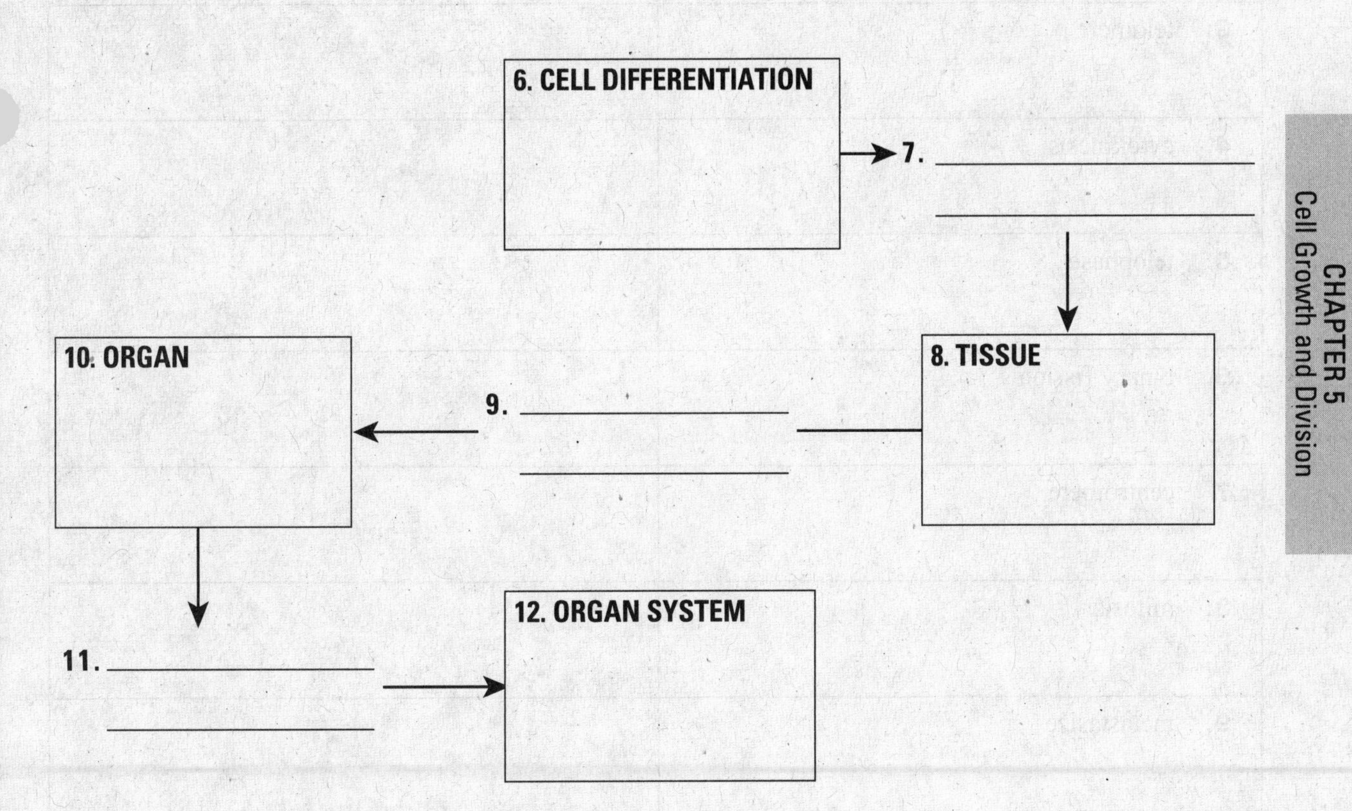

Name Period Date

VOCABULARY PRACTICE, CONTINUED

D. Word Origins Circle the Greek and Latin word parts in each vocabulary term. Then use the Greek and Latin meanings to construct a very basic definition of the vocabulary word.

bi-	=	two	mal-	=	bad, evil	pro-	=	at the start
centro-	=	middle	-mere	=	part, segment	telo-	=	end
cyto-	=	cell	meta-	=	change; occurring after			
kin-	=	movement	mitos-	=	thread			

WORD	DEFINITION
1. malignant	
2. prophase	
3. telomere	
4. cytokinesis	
5. telophase	
6. binary fission	
7. centromere	
8. mitosis	
9. metastasize	
10. metaphase	

CHAPTER 5
Cell Growth and Division

UNIT 2 | *CELL*EBRATION MINI GOLF

Unit Project

Your school district wants to increase funding for its science labs. A local biotechnology company has offered to pay for the construction of a mini-golf course, with proceeds to go to the school district. The biotech company wants to get the local community interested in biology and have decided to hold a design contest. Participants must design a 12-hole miniature-golf course modeled after a cell (plant or animal) with different cell organelles and structures realistically incorporated into the design of each hole. In order for designs to be considered, blueprints, a proposal letter, and a presentation must be submitted to the biotech company by the proposal deadline.

Directions for the blueprints and the proposal letter are as follows:

- The holes of the mini-golf course should have **TWELVE** of the following cell organelles or structures represented: cell membrane, vesicle, nucleus, nucleolus, endoplasmic reticulum, Golgi apparatus, mitochondrion, vacuole, nuclear envelope, ribosome, microtubules, and microfilaments. Additionally, if the design is based on an **animal** cell, a centriole and lysosome must be included; if based on a **plant** cell, a chloroplast and cell wall must be included.
- Incorporate the organelle's structure or function into your design. For example, the vacuole could be a water feature; the endoplasmic reticulum could have a tube that transports the golf ball to another location.
- Make a blueprint that shows the layout of the course and the relative shape and size of each organelle. Your blueprint can be drawn on a posterboard or done electronically. If electronic, you must also submit your drawings – do not copy information from the Internet and call it your own.
- On your blueprint, identify the number for each hole, each organelle, and its **function.** Briefly describe the **appearance** of each organelle's hole.
- The path that leads from one hole to the next should link organelles whose functions relate to one another.
- In your proposal letter, describe your idea behind the design and clearly explain how the functions of the organelles that link together relate to one another.
- Both the blueprint and the proposal letter should be neat, organized, and easy to read.

Name Period Date

UNIT 2 Cells

*Cell*ebration Mini Golf Evaluation Rubric

Points will be assigned according to how well a task is done, as well as whether you have fully or only partially completed a task. Any task left undone will be assigned a zero. Your teacher will provide a timetable for this project.

Requirements	Maximum Points	Earned Points (teacher to fill in)
Proposal		
Proposal is neat, typewritten and spell-checked.	5	
Design and relationship between linked organelles is clearly explained.	25	
Blueprint		
Blueprint is on posterboard, neat, spell-checked, and colorful.	10	
All 12 organelles are present.	10	
Holes are identified by organelle name and number.	5	
Organelle function is correctly described.	15	
Organelle appearance is correctly described.	10	
Organelle's relative shape is accurately represented.	10	
Organelle's relative size is accurately represented.	10	
Rubric Score:	100 points	
Extra Credit (given at the teacher's discretion):		
Determine a price structure for the golf course and project yearly revenues.		
	Total Score:	
Teacher's Comments:		

UNIT 2 | *CELL*EBRATION MINI GOLF

Unit Project Teacher Notes

Purpose: To understand the structure and function of cell organelles and the relationships between them.

Overview: Students will design a mini-golf course that models a cell. They will:

- Incorporate the main cell organelles from either a plant or animal cell
- Identify the size, structure, and function of each organelle
- Identify and explain the relationships between different organelles

Preparation:

- Copy project description, student handout (optional), and rubric
- Plan timetable

Project Management:

- Assign project at the beginning of Chapter 3.
- Hand out the project sheet and review it with the class.
- Projects are done out of class and should take three weeks to complete.
- Project can be done individually or in small groups. Be sure students working in groups realize that they are responsible for working together on the project **outside** of class.
- Chapter 3, section 3.2 contains key information that relates to the project.
- You may want to supply students with websites that provide information and pictures of cell organelles and mini-golf courses.
- For students who have difficulty compiling information or are overwhelmed with the content, provide them with copies of the student handout provided.
- You may want to set aside 10 to 15 minutes a couple of times a week to allow students to collaborate with partners, or to seek your assistance.
- The presentation component to this project can be optional or offered as extra credit.
- Have students check in weekly to monitor their progress.

Differentiation: This project can be adapted for various ability levels within the class.

- **Below Level Students:** Reduce the number of holes from 12 to 6.
- **Pre-AP Students:** In place of a blueprint, have students build a 3-dimensional scale model of the mini-golf course. All calculations must be accurate and included on the model.

Student Handout

Cell Organelle Descriptions and Sizes

Organelle or Structure	Function	Appearance
Cytoskeleton	Supports and shapes the cell. The cytoskeleton includes: microtubules (gives cell its shape and assists in organelle movement) and microfilaments (enable cells to move and divide)	Microtubules are long, hollow tubes. Microfilaments are tiny, threadlike structures.
Cell Membrane	Forms a boundary between the cell and the outside environment and controls the passage of materials into and out of the cell	Outermost layer in an animal cell; second layer in a plant cell
Nucleus	Storehouse for most of the cell's genetic information	Round
Nuclear Envelope	Protects the nucleus and allows large molecules to pass between the nucleus and cytoplasm through pores	Surrounds the nucleus and has holes (pores)
Nucleolus	Produces ribosomes	Round structure inside the nucleus
Endoplasmic Reticulum	Produces, processes, and distributes proteins	Irregular, maze-like (could be bumpy if depicting Rough ER, or smooth if depicting Smooth ER)
Ribosomes	Form proteins	Small, round structures that may be attached to the ER or suspended in the cytoplasm
Golgi Apparatus	Process, sort, and deliver proteins	Layered stack
Vesicles	Isolate and transport materials within the cell	Round
Mitochondria	Supply energy to the cell	Bean–shaped
Vacuole	Temporarily stores materials the cell needs (water, food, inorganic ions, and enzymes)	Fluid–filled sac
Lysosomes (Animal cells only)	Digest and recycle foreign materials or worn–out parts	Small, irregularly shaped
Centrioles (Animal cells only)	Aids in mitosis	Cylinder–shaped, made of short microtubules arranged in a circle; two are present, arranged perpendicular to one another

Organelle or Structure	Function	Appearance
Cell Wall (Plant cells only)	Gives protection, support, and shape to the cell	Rigid, outermost layer of a plant cell
Chloroplast (Plant cells only)	Converts solar energy to chemical energy through photosynthesis	Green, oval–shaped

Approximate Sizes of Cell Organelles

Organelle or Structure	Approximate Size*
Microfilament	6 nm
Cell membrane (thickness)	10 nm
Ribosome	11 nm
Cell Wall	20 nm
Microtubule	25 nm
Vesicle	30 nm
Endoplasmic Reticulum (tube diameter)	150 nm
Centriole	200 nm
Lysosome	200–500 nm
Golgi Body	2500 nm
Nucleolus	1000 nm
Mitochondrion	3000 nm
Chloroplast (length)	5000 nm
Nucleus	6000 nm
Vacuole	4000 nm (animal) 20000 nm (plant)

* Size can vary greatly from one cell to another. Use only as a guide to relative size.

Answer Key

Section 3.1

Study Guide

1. first to identify cells and name them
2. observed live cells and observed greater detail
3. concluded that plants are made of cells
4. concluded that animals and, in fact, all living things are made of cells
5. proposed that all cells come from other cells

6. All organisms are made of cells. All existing cells are produced by other living cells. The cell is the most basic unit of life.
7. Answers will vary. Sample answer: Cell theory is one of the great unifying theories of biology. Cell theory helped people understand that life didn't arise from nonliving sources.

Y diagram: *Eukaryotic cells*—surrounded by a cell membrane; contains cytoplasm; contains a nucleus; contains membrane-bound organelles; tends to be microscopic in size; eukaryotic organisms may be single-celled or multicellular; *Prokaryotic cells*—surrounded by a cell membrane; contains cytoplasm; tends to be microscopic in size; prokaryotic organisms are single-celled; *Both*—surrounded by a cell membrane; contains cytoplasm; tends to be microscopic in size.

8. a jellylike substance that contains dissolved molecular building blocks and, in some types of cells, organelles
9. in the cytoplasm
10. cell theory
11. prokaryotic cells

Power Notes

Scientists Who Contributed to the Cell Theory: Hooke, Leeuwenhoek, Schleiden, Schwann, Virchow
Important Technological Advances: Improvements in the microscope, such as better lenses
The Principles of Cell Theory: All organisms are made of cells. All existing cells are produced by other living cells. The cell is the most basic unit of life.
The Cell Theory: one of the first unifying concepts developed in biology.
This is a eukaryotic cell.
Labels: (top) nucleus, organelles; (bottom): DNA, cytoplasm, cell membrane
This is a prokaryotic cell.
All cells have a membrane, cytoplasm, and similar building blocks.

Reinforcement

1. the cell
2. in the cytoplasm; in the nucleus
3. They are tiny and consist of single cells.
4. All existing cells are produced by other living cells.

Section 3.2

Study Guide

1. The cytoskeleton supports and shapes the cell, positions and transports organelles, provides strength, assists in cell division, and aids cell movement.
2. The cytoskeleton supports and shapes the cell.
3. The cytoskeleton helps the cell move.

4. stores most of the genetic information of a cell; contains the nucleolus, where ribosomes are assembled
5. endoplasmic reticulum
6. link amino acids together to form proteins
7. processes, sorts, and delivers proteins
8. vesicles
9. supply energy to the cell by converting molecules from food into usable energy
10. stores materials needed by a cell; may help provide support to plant cells
11. contains enzymes that break down damaged and worn-out cell parts; defends a cell from invaders
12. organizes microtubules to form cilia and flagella for cell motion or the movement of fluids past a cell

13. The cell walls are strong and rigid and adhere to each other, which helps to support the entire plant.
14. All cells are surrounded by a cell membrane that is flexible and interacts with the environment. Only certain cells have a cell wall, which is rigid and provides shape and support to cells.
15. They enable plants to convert solar energy into energy-rich molecules that cells can use.
16. endoplasmic reticulum
17. mitochondrion

Power Notes

cytoskeleton: give shape, act as tracks for the movement of organelles, aid division, give strength, aid movement
nucleus: stores and protects the DNA
endoplasmic reticulum: production of proteins and lipids, breakdown of drugs and alcohol
ribosomes: link amino acids together to form proteins
Golgi apparatus: processes, sorts, and delivers proteins
vesicles: sacs that separate some materials from the rest of the cytoplasm, generally short-lived
mitochondria: supply energy to the cell by converting molecules from food into usable energy
vacuole: sac used for storage of materials, typically quite large in plant cells
lysosomes: sacs containing enzymes that defend a cell from invaders and break down worn-out cell parts
centrioles: consist of microtubules arranged in a circle; organize microtubules to form cilia and flagella; role in cell division not entirely clear
cell wall: rigid layer surrounding the cell membrane in plant, algae, fungi, and most bacteria cells; provides protection, support, and shape
chloroplasts: carry out photosynthesis to convert solar energy into energy-rich molecules

Reinforcement

1. eukaryotic are highly organized structures that are surrounded by a protective membrane that receive messages from other cells; they contain membrane-bound organelles that perform specific cellular processes
2. mitochondria supply energy to the cell
3. cells walls and chloroplasts

Section 3.3

Study Guide

1. Student should draw and label: phosphate group; glycerol; fatty acid.
2. the charged phosphate and glycerol
3. the fatty acid tails
4. polar
5. outside the cell because of the extracellular fluid and inside the cell because of the cytoplasm
6. The polar heads interact with the watery environments both inside and outside the cell. The nonpolar tails interact with each other inside the membrane.
7. strengthen the cell membrane
8. help materials cross the membrane, part of the cytoskeleton
9. help identify cell types
10. The phospholipids in each layer can move from side to side and slide past each other.
11. Refer to Figure 3.18 for visual answer.
12. receptor
13. ligand
14. intracellular
15. membrane, changes
16. The fluid mosaic model is a description of the arrangement of the molecules that make up a cell membrane. It emphasizes both the fluidity of the membrane and the variety of molecules that make up the membrane.
17. selective permeability

Power Notes

Cell membrane

Functions: contains cell contents, controls what enters and exits a cell
Fluid mosaic model: describes the arrangement of molecules making up a cell membrane; the membrane is flexible like a fluid and has a variety of molecules like the variety of tiles in a mosaic
Phospholipids: form a double layer surrounding a cell; composed of a charged phosphate group, glycerol, and two fatty acid chains; head is polar and forms hydrogen bonds with water; tail is nonpolar
Other molecules: cholesterol strengthens membranes, proteins aid cell identification and movement of molecules across membranes and cell signaling, carbohydrates aid cell identification
The sketch should look similar to Figure 3.18.
Selective permeability: allows some materials to cross; can also use terms such as semipermeable and selectively permeable; enables a cell to maintain homeostasis; molecules can cross in a variety of ways
Receptors: detect a signal molecule and perform an action in response
Intracellular: located inside a cell; bind to molecules that can cross the membrane
Membrane: located in the membrane; binds to molecules than cannot cross the membrane; change in shape transmits the message to the cell interior

Reinforcement

1. because this enables the polar heads to interact with the watery environments inside and outside the cell and allows the nonpolar tails to pack together inside the membrane, away from the water
2. A sieve allows certain molecules, such as water, to pass through but not other things like berries or noodles.

Section 3.4

Study Guide

1. the difference in the concentration of a substance from one location to another
2. The molecule diffuses from an area of higher concentration into an area of lower concentration.
3. diffusion
4. osmosis
5. the movement of molecules down a concentration gradient
6. the natural motion of particles
7. energy from the cell
8. lower
9. hypertonic
10. hypotonic
11. It occurs through selective transport proteins, not simply across the membrane.
12. down a concentration gradient
13. concentration gradient
14. Just as a hyper person has a higher level of energy than most people, a hypertonic solution has a higher level of solutes than the solution it is being compared to.
15. The transport protein makes it easier for a molecule that cannot directly cross the cell membrane to enter or exit a cell.

Power Notes

The figure should look similar to Figure 3.21.
Passive transport: the movement of molecules across a membrane without energy input from the cell
Diffusion: movement of molecules from higher to lower concentration
Osmosis: the diffusion of water
How do different solutions affect cells?
The figure should look similar to Figure 3.23; isotonic, hypertonic, hypotonic.
Facilitated diffusion: the diffusion of molecules across a membrane through transport proteins; requires no energy input from the cell
The figure should look similar to Figure 3.24.

Reinforcement

1. hypotonic, isotonic, hypertonic
2. Side A. The sugar cannot cross, but the water can diffuse. The water has a higher concentration on side A and a lower concentration on side B, so it diffuses from A to B.

Section 3.5

Study Guide

1. Active transport is the movement of molecules against a concentration gradient, whereas any type of diffusion is the movement of molecules down a concentration gradient.
2. Both involve the movement of molecules through selective membrane proteins.
3. All transport proteins span the membrane, and most change shape when they bind to a target molecule or molecules.
4. Active transport proteins use chemical energy to move a substance against its concentration gradient.
5. Refer to Figure 3.25 for visual answer.
6. ATP
7. vesicles
8. lysosomal enzymes

Y diagram:
Endocytosis—uses energy, takes substances into a cell, moves substances in vesicles; *Exocytosis*—uses energy, releases substances outside a cell, moves substances in vesicles; *Both*—use energy, move substances in vesicles.

9. phagocytosis
10. Exocytosis is a process that releases substances outside a cell. Endocytosis is a process that takes substances into a cell.
11. active transport

Power Notes

The figure should look similar to Figure 3.25.
Active transport: drives molecules across a membrane from lower to higher concentration (against a concentration gradient)
Endocytosis: process of taking in liquids or larger molecules into a cell by engulfing in a vesicle; requires energy
The diagram (1., 2. 3.) should look similar to the diagram on page 90 of the text.
Exocytosis: process of releasing substances out of a cell by fusion of a vesicle with the membrane
The diagram (1., 2. 3.) should look similar to the diagram on page 91 of the text.

Reinforcement

1. They all require energy and can move substances regardless of a concentration gradient.
2. In active transport, a material is moved through a transport protein. Endocytosis and exocytosis can move large materials in vesicles. The material does not actually cross the membrane.
3. releases hormones and digestive enzymes; transmits nerve impulses.

Chapter 3

Data Analysis Practice

1. The time, in minutes, it takes for equilibrium to be reached between the two sides of the aquarium.
2. The greater the concentration of solutes, the faster diffusion occurs.
3. Higher. Some of the water would diffuse from the side with 5% NaCl into the side with 30% NaCl, because the concentration of water molecules is higher in the side with 5% NaCl than in the side with 30% NaCl.

Pre-AP Activity

EXPERIMENT WITH OSMOSIS

1. Water molecules entered the potato cells because there was a higher concentration of solute in the potato than in the solution.
2. Water molecules moved out of the potato cells because there was a lower concentration of solute in the potato than in the solution.

3. Students should find that one of the potato pieces (in 1% salt solution) did not change in mass. Water molecules moved in and out of this potato piece's cells at an equal rate because the concentrations of solute in both solutions were equal.
4. The distilled water and 0.5% salt solution were hypotonic, and the 5% and 10% salt solutions were hypertonic.
5. The concentration of solutes in potato cells is about 1%, because in the 1% salt solution the concentrations of solutes inside and outside the potato were the same (isotonic).

Vocabulary Practice

A. Word Origins

1. taking of substances into a cell in vesicles
2. removal of substances out of a cell in vesicles
3. cell eating
4. the state of having more solutes compared to another solution
5. the state of having fewer solutes compared to another solution
6. the state of having an equal amount of solutes compared to another solution
7. an organelle that loosens, or breaks down, molecules and cellular components
8. a green organelle that contains chlorophyll and is involved in photosynthesis
9. the jellylike substance composed of water and dissolved molecules and ions that fills much of a cell
10. the skeleton of a cell; an interconnected network of proteins that gives a cell strength, the ability to move, and the ability to transport organelles

B. Analogies

1. ribosomes
2. cell wall
3. selective permeability
4. passive transport
5. active transport
6. exocytosis
7. concentration gradient
8. Golgi apparatus
9. nucleus
10. Sample answer: The cytoskeleton is sort of like the underlying structure of a building that holds everything else up and provides a structure for elevators to run up and down.
11. Sample answer: Phagocytosis is sort of like a person who hovers over the food, shoveling in huge bites.

C. Vector Vocabulary

1. the movement of molecules across a membrane through a transport protein requiring energy input from a cell
2. the movement of molecules across a membrane without energy input from a cell
3. the diffusion of molecules across the cell membrane is a type of passive transport
4. the movement of molecules from a region of higher concentration to a region of lower concentration
5. the movement of water molecules from a region of higher water concentration to a region of lower water concentration
6. osmosis is the diffusion of water molecules
7. the relative concentrations of two solutions separated by a semipermeable membrane will determine the direction of osmosis across the membrane
8. having an equal amount of solutes compared to another solution
9. having fewer solutes compared to another solution
10. have more solutes compared to another solution

D. Who Am I?

1. organelles
2. cell theory
3. phospholipids
4. fluid mosaic model
5. eukaryotic cell
6. prokaryotic cell
7. facilitated diffusion
8. endoplasmic reticulum
9. lysosomes
10. mitochondrion
11. centriole
12. cell membrane
13. receptor
14. vacuole
15. vesicle

Section 4.1

Study Guide

1. adenosine triphosphate (ATP)

2. a molecule that transfers energy from the breakdown of food molecules to cell processes
3. ATP is a high-energy molecule that is converted into lower-energy ADP when a phosphate group is removed and energy is released. ADP is converted back into ATP by the addition of a phosphate group.

   Cycle Diagram: High-energy adenosine triphosphate (ATP); Phosphate removed, energy released; Lower-energy adenosine diphosphate (ADP); Energy added from breakdown of carbon-based molecules, phosphate added.

4. molecules most commonly broken down; glucose yields about 36 ATP; 4 calories per mg (4 Calories per gram)
5. store most of the energy in a person's body; triglyceride yields about 146 ATP; 9 calories per mg (9 Calories per gram)
6. least likely to be broken down; store about the same amount of energy as carbohydrates; 4 calories per mg (4 Calories per g)
7. a process by which some organisms use chemical energy instead of light energy to make energy-storing carbon-based molecules
8. ATP has three phosphate groups; ADP has two phosphate groups.
9. Together, they mean "to put together with chemicals." In chemosynthesis, chemical energy is used to produce carbon-based molecules that store energy.

Power Notes

1. ATP
2. energy released for cell processes
3. ADP
4. energy from breakdown of molecules
5. 4 cal/mg; 36 ATP from glucose; most common molecule broken down to make ATP
6. 9 cal/mg; 146 ATP from a triglyceride; stores most of the energy in people
7. 4 cal/mg; infrequently broken down by cells to make ATP

   Chemosynthesis—process through which some organisms use chemicals from the environment (rather than light energy) as a source of energy to build carbon-based molecules

Reinforcement

1. to transfer chemical energy from the breakdown of molecules in food to cell processes
2. a lower-energy molecule that is converted into ATP by the addition of a phosphate group
3. carbohydrates, lipids, proteins

Section 4.2

Study Guide

1. they produce the source of chemical energy for themselves and for other organisms
2. to capture light energy to make sugars that store chemical energy
3. a molecule in chloroplasts that absorbs some of the energy in visible light
4. membrane-bound organelles where photosynthesis takes place in plants
5. stroma and grana
6. coin-shaped, membrane-enclosed compartments inside the grana
7. $6CO_2 + 6H_2O \rightarrow\rightarrow\rightarrow\rightarrow C_6H_{12}O_6 + 6O_2$ Carbon dioxide and water (the reactants) enter photosynthesis. Through many chemical reactions, with the help of many enzymes, a six-carbon sugar and oxygen (the products) are formed.
8. The light-dependent reactions require light, and they absorb and transfer energy. The light-independent reactions do not directly need light, and they build sugars.

   Labels for Chloroplast Steps: (1) Energy from sunlight is absorbed and transferred along the thylakoid membrane. Water molecules are broken down and oxygen is released. (2) Energy carried along the thylakoid membrane is transferred to molecules that carry energy to the light-independent reactions. (3) Carbon dioxide is added to a cycle of chemical reactions to build larger molecules. (4) A six-carbon simple sugar (usually glucose; $C_6H_{12}O_6$) is formed.

9. Energy from light is used to put sugars together.
10. Chlorophyll is the light-absorbing molecule that makes leaves look green.
11. The light-dependent reactions require sunlight; the light-independent reactions can occur without sunlight.

Power Notes

Photosynthesis—process through which light energy is captured and used to build sugars that store chemical energy

1. chloroplast
2. sunlight
3. water
4. thylakoid; chlorophyll and other light-absorbing molecules
5. oxygen
6. energy-carrying molecules transferred to light-independent reactions
7. carbon dioxide from the atmosphere
8. light-independent reactions (Calvin cycle)
9. one six-carbon sugar (glucose)

Photosynthesis equation

$6CO_2 + 6H_2O \Rightarrow\Rightarrow\Rightarrow\Rightarrow\Rightarrow C_6H_{12}O_6 + 6O_2$

Reinforcement

1. a process that captures energy from sunlight to make sugars that store chemical energy
2. in the stroma and grana of chloroplasts
3. Energy is absorbed from sunlight and transferred to molecules that carry energy. Water molecules are broken down and oxygen is released.
4. Energy from the light-dependent reactions is used to build sugars from carbon dioxide.
5. carbon dioxide and water (reactants); sugars and oxygen (products)

Section 4.3

Study Guide

1. to capture and transfer energy
2. groups of molecules that capture and transfer energy
3. ATP and NADPH

Steps for Sequence Diagram: (1) Chlorophyll (in the thylakoid membrane) absorbs energy from sunlight and energized electrons enter the electron transport chain. (2) Water molecules are broken down. Oxygen is released as waste and electrons enter chlorophyll. (3) Energy from electrons in the transport chain is used to pump hydrogen ions across the thylakoid membrane. (4) More energy is absorbed and transferred to electrons. (5) Energized electrons leave the electron transport chain and are used to produce NADPH. (6) Hydrogen ions flow through a channel coupled to ATP synthase. (7) ATP synthase produces ATP.

4. to use energy from the light-dependent reactions to convert carbon dioxide into sugars

Calvin Cycle steps: (1) Carbon dioxide is added to the Calvin cycle. (2) Energy is used to split six-carbon molecules. Three-carbon molecules are formed and rearranged. (A) A three-carbon molecule exits the cycle. Other three-carbon molecules stay in the cycle. (3) When two three-carbon molecules have left the cycle they bond to form a six-carbon sugar (glucose). (4) Energy is used to convert the remaining three-carbon molecules into five-carbon molecules.

5. a series of proteins in the thylakoid membrane along which energized electrons travel
6. It is an enzyme that synthesizes ATP.

7. the reactions go from one to another with no beginning or end

Power Notes

1. energy absorbed from sunlight and transferred to electrons that enter an electron transport chain
2. water molecules are broken down; electrons enter chlorophyll
3. energy from electrons in transport chain is used to pump H^+ ions across the thylakoid membrane
4. energy absorbed from sunlight is transferred to electrons
5. high-energy electrons used to produce an energy-carrying molecule called NADPH
6. H^+ ions flow (by diffusion) through a channel in the thylakoid membrane
7. The channel is part of ATP synthase, which produces ATP

1. carbon dioxide molecules enter the Calvin cycle
2. energy added to molecules in the cycle; molecules rearranged into higher-energy molecules
3. high-energy three-carbon molecule leaves the cycle; two are bonded together to make a six-carbon sugar
4. energy added to molecules remaining in the cycle to change them into five-carbon molecules

Reinforcement

1. photosystem II, photosystem I, and ATP synthase
2. absorb energy and transfer energy to electrons that go into the electron transport chain; break down water; pump hydrogen ions across the thylakoid membrane
3. absorb energy and transfer energy to electrons in the electron transport chain; produce NADPH to carry energy
4. to produce ATP as hydrogen ions flow through the enzyme
5. A series of chemical reactions use ATP and NADPH from the light-dependent reactions to make high-energy sugars from low-energy carbon dioxide.

Section 4.4

Study Guide

1. a process that releases energy from sugars and other carbon-based molecules to make ATP when oxygen is present
2. it needs oxygen to take place
3. in mitochondria
4. In the cytoplasm, a molecule of glucose is split into two three-carbon molecules and 2 ATP are formed.
5. cellular respiration breaks down sugars to make ATP; the overall chemical equations are the reverse of each other
6. matrix and inner mitochondrial membrane
7. $C_6H_{12}O_6 + 6O_2 \rightarrow\rightarrow\rightarrow\rightarrow\rightarrow\rightarrow 6CO_2 + 6H_2O$
8. A six-carbon sugar (such as glucose) and oxygen (the reactants) enter the cellular respiration process. Through a series of chemical reactions, ATP is produced, and carbon dioxide and water (the products) are formed.

Steps of Cellular Respiration: (1) Three-carbon molecules enter the Krebs cycle and are broken down. ATP and other energy-carrying molecules are formed. Carbon dioxide is released as a waste product. (2) Energy is transferred to the second stage of cellular respiration (the electron transport chain). (3) Energized electrons are passed along the electron transport chain in the inner mitochondrial membrane. (4) A large number of ATP are formed. Oxygen picks up electrons, and water is released as a waste product.

9. A sugar (sweet) is broken down (loosened) during glycolysis.
10. It is a process that takes place without oxygen.
11. a cycle of chemical reactions that breaks down carbon-based molecules

to transfer energy to the electron transport chain

Power Notes

Cellular respiration — process through which sugars and other carbon-based molecules are broken down to produce ATP when oxygen is available

Glycolysis—anaerobic process in cytoplasm that splits glucose into 2 three-carbon molecules

1. mitochondrion
2. three-carbon molecules
3. Krebs cycle; mitochondrial matrix; produces 2 ATP
4. carbon dioxide
5. energy transferred to 2nd aerobic stage
6. energy from glycolysis and oxygen enter the process
7. water produced; large number of ATP molecules produced

Cellular respiration equation:
$C_6H_{12}O_6 + 6O_2 \Rightarrow\Rightarrow\Rightarrow\Rightarrow\Rightarrow$
$6CO_2 + 6H_2O$

Reinforcement

1. the process that breaks down sugars and other carbon-based molecules to make ATP when oxygen is present
2. Glycolysis splits glucose into two three-carbon molecules and yields a net increase of two ATP molecules. The process does not require oxygen.
3. The Krebs cycle breaks down three-carbon molecules to make ATP, energy-carrying molecules, and carbon dioxide waste.
4. to make a large number of ATP molecules using energy-carrying molecules from the Krebs cycle

Section 4.5

Study Guide

1. to split glucose and produce energy-carrying molecules
2. Pyruvate and NADH are used in cellular respiration; ATP can be used for cell processes.
3. 2 ATP are used to split glucose, and 4 are produced, resulting in a net gain of 2 ATP
4. to produce energy-carriers from the breakdown of carbon-based molecules

   Krebs Cycle: (1) Coenzyme A binds to two-carbon molecule; enters Krebs cycle. (2) Citric acid formed. (3) Citric acid broken down, carbon dioxide released, NADH produced. (4) Five-carbon molecule broken down, carbon dioxide released, NADH and ATP produced. (5) Four-carbon molecule rearranged, NADH and $FADH_2$ produced
5. inner mitochondrial membrane
6. to use energy from electrons to pump hydrogen ions across the membrane, so that the ions can flow back through ATP synthase to produce ATP

   Electron Transport Chain: high-energy electrons removed from NADH and $FADH_2$ by proteins in the transport chain. (2) energy from the electrons used to pump hydrogen ions across the inner mitochondrial membrane. (3) hydrogen ions flow through ATP synthase; ATP is produced. (4) oxygen picks up electrons from the transport chain and hydrogen ions; water is produced and released.
7. Oxygen picks up electrons at the end of the electron transport chain; without oxygen to pick up the electrons, cellular respiration stops.

Power Notes

Glycolysis (as a sketch or in words)—2 ATP molecules used to split glucose; 4 ATP (2 ATP net) and 2 NADH formed as the three-carbon molecules are rearranged into 2 molecules of pyruvate

1. pyruvate broken down; CO_2 released
2. coenzyme A binds; intermediate enters Krebs cycle
3. citric acid (6-carbon molecule) formed
4. citric acid broken down; NADH made; CO_2 released

5. five-carbon molecule broken down; NADH and ATP made; CO_2 released
6. four-carbon molecule rearranged, NADH and $FADH_2$ made
7. Krebs cycle (or citric acid cycle)

1. energized electrons removed from NADH and $FADH_2$
2. energy from electrons in the electron transport chain is used to pump H^+ ions across the inner mitochondrial membrane
3. H^+ ions flow through ATP synthase, and ATP molecules are produced
4. oxygen picks up electrons that went through the electron transport chain and H^+ ions

Reinforcement

1. Two ATP molecules are used to split glucose. Pyruvate, two ATP (net), and two NADH molecules are produced.
2. Pyruvate is broken down and enters the Krebs cycle. The Krebs cycle breaks down and rearranges carbon-based molecules to produce ATP, energy-carrying molecules, and carbon dioxide waste.
3. to use energy from energized electrons to produce ATP
4. It picks up electrons that travel along the electron transport chain.
5. glucose and oxygen are the reactants; carbon dioxide and water are the products

Section 4.6

Study Guide

1. Fermentation allows glycolysis to continue making ATP when oxygen is unavailable for cellular respiration.
2. Fermentation removes electrons from NADH and recycles NAD^+ to glycolysis.
3. during hard exercise, when not enough oxygen is available
4. because it occurs without oxygen
5. fermentation allows glycolysis to take place, which yields 2 net ATP

Lactic Acid Fermentation: pyruvate and glycolysis enter fermentation; NADH is used to convert pyruvate into lactic acid; NADH is changed into NAD^+; NAD^+ is recycled to glycolysis

Alcoholic Fermentation: pyruvate and glycolysis enter fermentation; NADH is used to convert pyruvate into alcohol and carbon dioxide; NADH is changed into NAD^+; NAD^+ is recycled to glycolysis

6. Both use pyruvate and NADH and recycle NAD^+ to glycolysis. Lactic acid fermentation produces lactic acid as a waste product; alcoholic fermentation produces an alcohol and carbon dioxide.
7. cheese, yogurt
8. bread
9. Bubbles of carbon dioxide are produced during alcoholic fermentation.
10. the three-carbon waste product of lactic acid fermentation that causes a burning feeling in muscles during exercise

Power Notes

Fermentation—process that allows glycolysis to continue to produce ATP when oxygen is not available, but does not produce ATP

Lactic acid fermentation (as sketch or in words)—pyruvate and NADH enter fermentation; NADH used to convert pyruvate into lactic acid; NAD^+ recycled to glycolysis

Alcoholic fermentation (as sketch or in words)—pyruvate and NADH enter fermentation; NADH used to convert pyruvate into an alcohol and carbon dioxide; NAD^+ recycled to glycolysis

1. cheese
2. yogurt
3. bread

Reinforcement

1. Fermentation allows glycolysis to continue to produce ATP when oxygen is not available by removing electrons from NADH and recycling NAD^+ to glycolysis.
2. Both use energy from NADH to convert pyruvate

into a different product. Both recycle NAD^+ to glycolysis. Lactic acid fermentation produces lactic acid, whereas alcoholic fermentation produces an alcohol and carbon dioxide.

3. It is used in food production, such as yogurt and bread.

Chapter 4

Data Analysis Practice

1. low-light: 230 mg/g; moderate-light: 300 mg/g
2. In both groups as the time they are exposed to light increases, the amount of chlorophyll increases. For the first 12 hours the seedlings in low light have increasingly higher amounts of chlorophyll compared to the seedlings in moderate light. After 12 hours, however, the moderate light group surpasses the low light group in chlorophyll amounts.
3. Moderate light, because more chlorophyll will allow photosynthesis to take place at a higher rate.

Pre-AP Activity

LEAF STRUCTURE: BUILT FOR PHOTOSYNTHESIS

1. Carbon dioxide and water in the presence of sunlight produce sugar and oxygen.
2. The fact that epidermal cells are transparent enables sunlight to reach the inner layers of mesophyll cells. The waxy coating of the cells prevents water from evaporating. When the guard cells of a stoma are open, they enable carbon dioxide to reach the mesophyll cells and oxygen to escape. Students may mention that stomata prevent loss of water in dry weather.
3. The cells all have a large number of chloroplasts to carry out photosynthesis and produce sugars needed by the plant. The upper layer of palisade mesophyll has maximum exposure to the Sun and the tight packing ensures a high level of photosynthetic activity. The inner spongy mesophyll provides open space needed for water vapor and carbon dioxide to reach all the cells of the ground tissue and provides for the escape of oxygen.
4. Typically veins run either parallel or branch out from a central vein, either way spreading out to cover the whole area of the leaf.
5. On most trees, the leaves lie perpendicular to the rays of the Sun and spread out so upper leaves do not block all the light going to the leaves below.
6. natural selection

Pre-AP Activity

ORDER VERSUS DISORDER IN LIVING MATTER

1. The energy is not being used to do work, rather it is contributing to the increasing disorder, or entropy, in the universe.
2. It is decreasing since matter and energy are harnessed to contribute to a high degree of order.
3. Despite all the energy captured and stored in the living matter of an organism, heat is released, so the second law of thermodynamics has not been broken. By transforming and releasing heat energy, an organism can decrease its own entropy while contributing to the entropy of the universe.
4. Earth is an open system. The Sun releases vast amounts of solar energy into the solar system. As much energy as Earth's photosynthetic organisms capture and release, there is still more to be had.
5. The pyramid shrinks in size the higher it goes. A large number of producers at the base feed fewer and fewer animals as energy moves up through the pyramid because energy is lost as heat at each stage.
6. Using heat as a form of energy would simply increase the overall activity of all the molecules in the body in an indiscriminant

way, increasing entropy, not decreasing it.

Vocabulary Practice

A. Matching

1. thylakoid
2. Calvin cycle
3. electron transport chain
4. photosystem
5. light-dependent reaction
6. chlorophyll

B. Stepped-Out Vocabulary

1. a process that requires oxygen; takes place in mitochondria; takes place in all eukaryotes
2. process that splits glucose into 2 three-carbon molecules and produces 2 ATP; takes place in cytoplasm; does not require oxygen
3. a low-energy molecule that can be converted into ATP by the addition of a phosphate group; has two phosphate groups; changed into ATP by ATP synthase
4. process that allows glycolysis to continue but does not make ATP; types include alcoholic and lactic acid; recycles NAD^+ to glycolysis
5. releases chemical energy from carbon-based molecules (sugars) to make ATP when oxygen is available; takes place in mitochondria; occurs in all eukaryotes
6. a process that takes place without oxygen; includes glycolysis and fermentation; muscle cells use anaerobic processes during hard exercise
7. breaks down carbon-based molecules to transfer energy to an electron transport chain; produces carbon dioxide as a waste product; makes 2 ATP
8. product of fermentation that causes muscles to "burn"; waste product made in cells of vertebrates and some microorganisms; makes yogurt

C. Word Origins

1. relating to air
2. relating to no air
3. light system
4. put together with chemicals
5. put together with light
6. putting ATP together

D. Analogy Vocabulary Set

1. D2; A1
2. D5; A5
3. D1; A2
4. D4; A3
5. D3; A4

E. Do-It Yourself Matching

1. Sample answer: coin-shaped, membrane-enclosed compartments that make up grana
2. Sample answer: process that allows glycolysis to continue but does not produce ATP
3. Sample answer: process that uses energy from the light-dependent reactions to make sugars
4. Sample answer: takes place without oxygen
5. Sample answer: the waste product of lactic acid fermentation that produces a burning feeling in muscles
6. Sample answer: a process that uses chemical energy from the environment to make carbon-based molecules

F. Vector Vocabulary

1. process that splits glucose into two three-carbon molecules
2. when oxygen is available
3. process that breaks down carbon-based molecules to make ATP
4. chemical reactions in mitochondria
5. series of chemical reactions that produces energy-carrying molecules
6. energy transferred
7. energy from electrons used to produce ATP
8. when oxygen is not available
9. process that allows glycolysis to continue to produce a small amount of ATP
10. chemical reaction in cytoplasm
11. waste product of fermentation that causes muscles to "burn"

Section 5.1

Study Guide

Cell Cycle: (1) Gap 1 (G_1): cells grow, carry out normal functions, and copy their organelles. (2) Synthesis (S): cells replicate DNA. (3) Gap 2 (G_2): cells go through additional growth. (4) Mitosis (M): cells undergo cell division, which involves both the processes of mitosis and cytokinesis.

1. At the time that these stages were named, scientists could not observe any activity going on in cells, so they thought there were gaps in cellular activity.
2. G_1 and G_2
3. in the nucleus
4. mitosis and cytokinesis
5. G_1
6. The rate of cell division is linked to the body's need for that cell type. Skin cells are typically exposed to more damaging conditions and must be replaced more often than liver cells.
7. the name that some scientists give to the stage where cells carry out their normal functions but are unlikely to divide
8. Answers will vary. Sample answer: Cell size is limited because all substances must cross the membrane. Enough material needs to enter and exit to keep the cell alive. Since volume tends to increase faster than surface area (in a sphere or cube), the volume could quickly become too large compared to the area available for exchange. In a similar way, people in a very large theater that holds thousands might not be able to exit quickly for an emergency. People in a smaller theater that seats fewer people could probably exit more quickly.
9. volume
10. growth and division
11. Answers will vary, but should relate the recurrence of something (steps, phases, the rotation of a wheel) to the repeating pattern of growth, DNA duplication, and cell division that occurs in eukaryotic cells.
12. cytokinesis; *cyto-* refers to a cell and *kinesis* refers to division or movement
13. mitosis

Power Notes

1. gap 1
2. cell growth, normal functions, replications of organelles
3. synthesis
4. copies DNA
5. gap 2
6. additional growth and carrying out of normal functions
7. mitosis
8. cell division
9. prophase
10. metaphase
11. anaphase
12. telophase
13. cytokinesis
14. mitosis
15. interphase

Cells divide at different rates
Rates of cell division vary widely and are linked to the body's need. The length of gap 1 varies most widely among cell types. Some cells, such as neurons, enter a stage called G_0, where cells are unlikely to divide again.

Cell size is limited
If cells were too small, they could not contain all the organelles and molecules necessary for life. If cells were too large, they could not move enough materials across the membrane surface. To maintain a suitable size, cell growth and division must be coordinated.

The smallest cube should be circled.

Reinforcement

1. G_1, S, G_2, M
2. mitosis and cytokinesis
3. Different cells receive different amounts of damage. The body only needs some cells to be replaced at a time.

Section 5.2

Study Guide

1. one long continuous thread of DNA that has many genes and regulatory information
2. so they can be more easily divided between the two nuclei
3. Proteins need to be able to access genes during other stages of the cell cycle so that they can be used to make proteins or so that the entire DNA sequence can be copied.

DNA Diagram: Refer to Figure 5.5 for visual answer.

4. During interphase, a cell duplicates its DNA and organelles.

5. body cells
6. Answers will vary. Sample answer: Pat's mom ate tomatoes.

Cycle Diagram: Refer to Figure 5.7 for visual answer. Labels (clockwise) metaphase, anaphase, telophase

7. In animal cells, the membrane pinches together, forming a cleavage furrow. In plant cells, the membrane cannot pinch together because of the cell wall. Instead, a cell plate is laid down between the two nuclei, which will develop into the new cell walls and cell membranes.

8. histones
9. chromatin
10. centromere
11. telomeres

Power Notes

Chromosome structure
A chromosome is one long continuous thread of DNA. DNA wraps around proteins called histones. DNA and histones form chromatin, which looks like spaghetti, during interphase. Chromosomes condense tightly for mitosis. Because they are duplicated, they look like an X.

1. interphase: copies DNA, grows, duplicates organelles
2. prophase: chromosomes condense, nuclear envelope breaks down, spindle fibers form
3. metaphase: spindle fibers align chromosomes along the cell equator
4. anaphase: chromatids separate to opposite sides of cell
5. telophase: nuclear membranes start to form around chromosomes, chromosomes begin to uncoil, spindle fibers fall apart
6. cytokinesis: divides the cytoplasm between two daughter cells

Reinforcement

1. They help organize and condense DNA.
2. one half of a duplicated chromosome
3. anaphase

Section 5.3

Study Guide

1. cell division
2. platelet-derived growth factor
3. specific cells

4. cyclins
5. kinases
6. phosphorylate
7. cell division

8. programmed cell death

9. cancer

Concept Map

a. tumors
b. benign
c. malignant
d. metastases

10. Mutations may be inherited, caused by chemicals and radiation, and carried by viruses.

11. to spread and grow by breaking away from a tumor
12. carcinogen
13. Answers will vary.

Power Notes

Internal factors: often triggered by external factors; include kinases and cyclins; kinases change the activity of other molecules by adding a phosphate group; cyclins are rapidly made and destroyed at different points in the cell cycle.

External factors: include cell-cell contact and other physical signals; also include chemical signals such as growth factors; growth factors may stimulate growth in a wide variety of cells or may stimulate only specific cells to divide

Carcinogens: substances that produce or promote the development of cancer; examples include tobacco smoke, air pollutants, radiation, and even some mutated genes carried by viruses

Cancer cells: characterized by uncontrolled cell

division; continue to grow despite cell-cell contact or lack of growth factors

Tumors: disorganized clumps of cancer cells that do not carry out specialized functions needed by the body

Malignant: cells break away and form new tumors
Benign: cells remain clustered together

Apoptosis: programmed cell death; plays a role in normal development and ridding the body of unhealthy cells
Example of apoptosis: cells between fingers

Reinforcement

1. growth factors and cell-cell contact
2. programmed cell death
3. A benign tumor stays in a clump. A malignant tumor has cells that break away and form new tumors in other parts of the body.

Section 5.4

Study Guide

1. Asexual reproduction produces genetically identical offspring. Sexual reproduction produces genetically unique offspring.
2. The bacterial chromosome is copied. Both copies attach to the cell membrane.
3. As the cell elongates, the chromosomes separate.
4. The membrane is pinched inward and a new wall is laid down. Refer to 5.4 Visual Vocab on page 148.
5. Advantages: Asexual reproduction can be more efficient under ideal circumstances. Disadvantages: Population may lack variety to survive in changing conditions.
6. Advantages: All organisms can potentially reproduce. Disadvantages: Not necessarily more efficient than sexual reproduction.
7. Advantages: No need to find a mate; no wasted energy attracting a mate. Disadvantages: Identical offspring all respond in same way to environment.
8. The two are genetically identical.
9. simpler plants and animals
10. budding, fragmentation, vegetative reproduction
11. sexually and asexually by dividing in half or breaking off small pieces from its base
12. Answers will vary. Students should recognize that "bi" indicates two. Binary fission is the division of a single-celled organism into two roughly equal parts.
13. asexual reproduction

Power Notes

Binary fission: asexual reproduction of a single-celled organism by division into two roughly equal parts; may sketch a figure similar to the Visual Vocab on page 148

Mitosis
Budding: small projection grows on surface of parent and forms a new organism
Fragmentation: parent organism splits into pieces that can each grow into a new organism
Vegetative reproduction: modification of a stem or underground structure from the parent organism; new organism often remains connected

Asexual reproduction: creation of genetically identical offspring from one parent organism; does not involve fusion of gametes

Advantages to species: Can be more efficient if organisms well suited to environment. All organisms can potentially reproduce. Organisms do not need to spend resources finding or attracting a mate.

Disadvantages to species: All organisms respond same way to environment. Organisms may lack adaptability to survive in changing conditions.

Reinforcement

1. offspring that are genetically identical to the parent organism and to the other offspring
2. Binary fission typically occurs in prokaryotic organisms; mitosis occurs in eukaryotic organisms.
3. All organisms are potentially capable of reproducing, and they don't

waste energy in trying to attract a mate.

Section 5.5

Study Guide

1. tissues
2. organs
3. organ systems
4. photosynthetic tissue; conductive tissue (e.g., xylem); protective tissue
5. shoot system; root system
6. These systems help organisms carry out complex, specialized functions and maintain homeostasis.
7. cell differentiation
8. No. All cells have the same DNA, but different types of cells express different sets of genes.
9. The location helps determine how the cell will differentiate.

Concept map:
a. origin
b. totipotent
c. pluripotent
d. multipotent
e. embryonic

10. divide and renew themselves for long periods of time; remain undifferentiated in form; develop into a variety of specialized cell types
11. Adult stem cells could avoid rejection issues and does not raise as many ethical concerns. Embryonic stem cells can develop into virtually any type of cell and can be grown indefinitely in culture.
12. the process by which an unspecialized cell becomes specialized
13. organ system, organ, tissue, cell

Power Notes

Organ systems: organs that carry out similar functions
Organs: groups of tissues that work together to perform similar or related functions
Tissues: groups of cells that work together to perform a similar function
Cells: smallest, most basic structural unit of life; typically become specialized

homeostasis: maintained by the interaction of different organ systems that coordinate the body's functions

Defining characteristics: ability to divide and renew themselves for long periods of time, remain undifferentiated in form, and can develop into a variety of specialized cell types.

Possible uses: treat patients with leukemia and lymphoma, may help cure diabetes, repair or replace damaged organs, and improve current drug testing techniques

Potential: Totipotent: can grow into any other cell type; includes only a fertilized egg and cells resulting from the first few divisions
Pluripotent: can grow into any cell type other than a totipotent stem cell
Multipotent: can only grow into cells of a closely related family of cells

Origin:
1. Adult stem cells; partially undifferentiated cells located among the specialized cells of many organs and tissues.
2. Embryonic stem cells: taken from clusters of undifferentiated cells in a 3–to-5–day-old embryo; pluripotent; can be grown indefinitely in culture

Reinforcement

1. the process by which unspecialized cells become specialized, or different from other cells
2. divide and renew themselves for long periods of time, remain undifferentiated in form, can develop into a variety of specialized cell types

Chapter 5

Data Analysis Practice

1. Students should construct a data table with columns for **Dosage (mg)** and **Patients with Side Effects (%).**
2. As the dosage increases, the percentage of patients with side effects increases.

Pre-AP Activity

SPINDLES AND MITOSIS

1. More polymerization occurs during prophase and metaphase because the spindle fibers have to extend out to reach the chromosomes; more depolymerization occurs during anaphase and telophase as the chromosomes are pulled towards opposite poles.
2. Colchicine would cause spindle fibers to stop growing and eventually break down; mitosis would stall since the spindle fibers would not be able to reach the chromosomes and pull them to opposite poles. Taxol would allow spindle fibers to grow but not shrink; mitosis would be disrupted because chromosomes would not be pulled to opposite poles.
3. These drugs would disrupt mitosis and prevent cancer cells from rapidly dividing.
4. Students should show tubulin subunits added to plus end of microtubule. The GTP cap should be a series of GTP subunits blocking the plus end of the microtubule.

Vocabulary Practice

A. Analogy Vocabulary Set

1. D5; A7
2. D3; A8
3. D1; A4
4. D6; A6
5. D4; A1
6. D7; A2
7. D8; A3
8. D2; A5

B. Compound Word Puzzle

1. prophase; Sample answer: nuclear envelope breaks down
2. stem cell; Sample answer: remains undifferentiated for long periods of time
3. metaphase; Sample answer: second phase of mitosis
4. telophase; Sample answer: nuclear envelope starts to form again
5. anaphase; Sample answer: third phase of mitosis
6. cancer; Sample answer: characterized by the formation of tumors
7. cytokinesis; Sample answer: cell membrane pinches together in animal cells
8. chromosome; Sample answer: a long continuous thread of DNA wrapped around organizing proteins

C. Vector Vocabulary

1. a substance that causes cancer
2. disrupts the cell cycle
3. the regular pattern of growth, DNA replication, and division of a cell
4. an out-of-control cell cycle can lead to cancer
5. a disease characterized by uncontrolled cell division
6. the process by which an undifferentiated cell becomes specialized
7. specialized cells can form increasingly complex structures
8. an organized group of cells that carry out a similar function
9. a group of related tissues form an organ
10. an organized group of tissues that carry out related functions
11. a group of related organs form an organ system
12. an organized group of organs that work together to coordinate various functions

D. Word Origins

1. describes a very bad tumor that spreads
2. the first phase of mitosis
3. the end part of a chromosome
4. the movement, or division, of a cell; specifically, the division of the cytoplasm and organelles
5. the end, or final, phase of mitosis
6. the division of a prokaryotic cell into two prokaryotic cells
7. the middle part of a chromosome that looks pinched together and is the place where sister chromatids are attached to each other
8. a process in which the chromosomes become visible like threads and are evenly divided between two nuclei
9. to change form by spreading to other parts of the body
10. the second phase of mitosis, occurring after the start of mitosis